TH

After Petula Hogan had walked out on
him Carl Elliot had become a changed
man, bitter and suspicious of all women.
So had Gail done the right thing in
agreeing to marry him? She had no
doubt about her feelings for Carl—but
would that be enough to make such a
one-sided marriage work?

Books you will enjoy
by MARGARET PARGETER

THE SILVER FLAME

After surviving the air crash, Jane was told she had been married to Colin Denyer who had lost his life in the crash—and as she had lost her memory she couldn't contradict Colin's disagreeable brother Paul. But what right had Paul to tell her, 'Don't imagine I'd be willing to step into Colin's shoes!' What made him think she wanted him to?

STORM IN THE NIGHT

Julia hadn't particularly wanted to be whisked off to live in France with some distant relatives, but she didn't really have much option—not, at least, if the forceful Guy Guerard had anything to do with it! And he could just drop this idea of finding a husband for her!

CHAINS OF REGRET

Because Helen hated her father's partner Stein Maddison so much she had run away from home—thinking, among other things, that he was a fortune-hunter. Now she was back, only to find that now the boot was on the other foot and that Stein had completely turned the tables on her. And why did he now seem to hate her so much?

NEVER GO BACK

Celia had disliked Guy Ryland for three years—ever since he had taken over her family's business, and she wasn't sure how she came now to be working for him. But then she wasn't sure about a lot of things—including the reason why she was so jealous of Guy's old friend Greta Morrison . . .

THE ODDS
AGAINST

BY

MARGARET PARGETER

MILLS & BOON LIMITED
15–16 BROOK'S MEWS
LONDON W1A 1DR

First published 1984
Australian copyright 1984
Philippine copyright 1984
This edition 1984

© Margaret Pargeter 1984

ISBN 0 263 74677 1

Set in Monophoto Times 10 on 10 pt.
01–0784 – 60021

Made and printed in Great Britain by
Richard Clay (The Chaucer Press) Ltd,
Bungay, Suffolk

CHAPTER ONE

GAIL knew she had been crazy to come out on such a night, in the middle of a snowstorm in the middle of March, but this didn't lessen her determination to reach Deanly. The roads were treacherous and every time she hit a particularly icy patch she thought, this is it! but amazingly she kept on going. Her small car responded to the reckless pressure of her foot with a heart worthy of a much larger vehicle.

Only another few miles, she prayed, wondering what Carl would say when he saw her. She was supposed to be staying overnight with her sister, Ruth. He would be furious with her for returning like this, just to apologise for being rude to him earlier. He had no patience with people who took foolish risks.

Unhappily Gail bit her lip. She would just have to let him believe she was a girl who never stopped to think, because she wouldn't dare tell him the real reason why she had come back. Her apologies could have waited, but when her intuition had told her that Carl was in some kind of danger, that was an entirely different matter! Once before on receiving such a message, from senses almost too sensitively tuned as far as he was concerned, she had found him alone and desperately in need of someone to help him. That was when he had broken his leg.

Many would have laughed at the very idea of Carl Elliot, with all the immense assurance of his thirty-six years and six foot two frame of superb masculinity being in any kind of trouble he couldn't handle—but then not everyone knew of the misfortunes which had beset him during the past year, including the biggest misfortune of the lot, Petula Hogan!

Petula Hogan. Gail's foot unwisely hit the accelerator

again, wishing it was Petula's head. How she hated her—although she had learned to disguise her feelings when Carl was around. For months he had worshipped her, and Petula had appeared to share his feelings. Certainly she had always been at the stables and never missed a race meeting with him if she could help it. Gaïl still found it difficult to believe how, after Carl had broken his leg and wasn't able to squire her around in the manner she was used to, Petula had swiftly succumbed to the attractions of an American millionaire who bred horses in the Blue Grass State of Kentucky.

The wedding had taken place six months ago, and while Gail knew that seeing Carl married to another woman might have finally broken her heart, she doubted if it could have been much worse than having to stand helplessly by, watching him suffer.

'She isn't worth it!' she had told him that very afternoon, catching him gazing at a small photograph of Petula which, despite her treachery, he apparently hadn't the willpower to throw away. He had looked so pale and grim, Gail had been driven to speak out.

'Can't you learn to mind your own business?' he had snarled, replacing the snap in his breast pocket.

Knowing he carried the image of someone who had betrayed him over his heart hurt so much she was stung to retort, 'I'd have thought a man like you would have had more pride!'

If anyone had dared to speak to him like this before he couldn't remember. His eyes had seared her furiously. 'You know nothing about a man like me.'

Indignation colouring her small, anxious face, Gail had replied rashly, 'I know you're one of the best owners in the country, and because you can't have—everything you'd like, you've stopped caring about anything else.'

'You're talking drivel!' he had retorted icily. 'I still breed horses, and now that my leg's better and your father's no longer here, don't I work all the hours God sends?'

'But you don't enjoy it,' Gail had cried bitterly, her green eyes tortured. 'Nothing really matters any more!'

'Aren't you thinking more of yourself?' he had accused savagely. 'You miss the excitement of rushing from one end of the country to the other.'

'You know it isn't that . . .' she began, then caught her bottom lip between confused white teeth, unable to put her sense of frustration in words which might penetrate the barrier of cold bitterness he seemed to hold between himself and the world. 'I'm sorry,' she whispered hopelessly.

'Are you?' he jeered sceptically, his dark blue gaze contemptuously holding her troubled green one. 'I wonder if you know the meaning of the word?'

'Of course I do . . .'

'If you don't stop prying into my affairs, you soon might!' Carl warned grimly. 'You'd better start remembering I employ you to work in my stables, not as an adviser on how to run my personal life.'

The threat in his voice had hurtled her from the house, hating him or wishing she could. She had shouted that she wouldn't be back and had flown straight to Ruth, vowing never to return—yet, only hours later, here she was!

A sob rose in Gail's throat as she drove blindly on, wondering what the future held for either of them. Five years ago, when she had been barely seventeen and her father had come to work as Carl's trainer, she had been delighted. She had loved Deanly on sight. It was so different from Lord Purdie's place, where she had lived all her life, that she could have jumped for joy. The Purdies, like the estate they had sold in order to retire, were cold, bleak people. The only time, Gail suspected, Lady Purdie had approved of her was when she was away at boarding school. At Deanly the whole atmosphere was different, even the horses seemed happier, and though for a while she had held its owner in considerable awe she hadn't found him at all frightening.

Her father, who had been rather down at having to leave Lord Purdie's stables, where he had been for so many years, had soon been impressed by him. 'He's more like half a dozen men,' he had declared, after the first week. 'It's no use trying to deceive him about anything, not even the little thing. What he doesn't know about the business he's in wouldn't be worth mentioning.'

'Do you think he knows as much about women?' Gail had asked scornfully, recalling how, the day before, a guest of Mr Elliot's, a redheaded beauty, had sorely tried the patience of the whole yard with her never-ending flow of idiotic remarks. Carl Elliot had appeared more interested in the girl's looks than in what she was saying and had merely smiled with warm tolerance while his staff fumed.

Her father had laughed and continued to laugh over the years as he'd watched the women come and go and Carl remained single. It wasn't until the arrival of Petula that he had stopped laughing and begun to worry. When she had married Lee Oscar, Gail had noticed him almost visibly relax, but his relief, like her own, had turned to despair when it soon became apparent how Petula's defection was affecting Carl.

In a way, Gail thought fiercely, as she battled through the snow, it was perhaps a blessing that a fatal heart attack had prevented her father from witnessing what looked like being Carl's final destruction. Everything was going to pieces and he didn't seem to care! It was true he still worked hard, but he refused to make the important decisions which were necessary for the successful running of the stables. And at times he would be away, simply disappearing so that no one could get in touch with him when a crisis arose. No training establishment could carry on without money, and already, because Carl hadn't been available to give his consent, they had missed several races where the rewards might almost have been guaranteed.

Sweeping a weary hand over tired eyes, Gail frowned

at the impotency of her own position. What more could she do? Despite what the others thought, she could only do so much. Carl might have spoiled her a little in the past, but those days were gone. The way things had been between them lately she expected at any time to be given her dismissal.

After her father had died, Carl let her stay on, but she had known it hadn't been important to him whether she did or not. Sean had been a brilliant trainer, working under contract, on a salary plus commission basis. Since his death, Carl hadn't bothered to find anyone to replace him, although Gail had urged him to. When approached he usually said he would get round to it in time, but he never did. He appeared to be quite content leaving the extra work and responsibility to Gail and the assistant trainer, who had only been with them a few months. Gail didn't mind, for she had picked up a lot of her father's expertise, but she had no fancy to step into his shoes, nor did she consider that Frank had the necessary experience either. As it was, the two of them, along with the head lad and yard secretary, were just about managing to cope.

Gail suspected that Carl had almost stopped going to race meetings for fear of bumping into Petula, who was occasionally over here with her husband. Gail had been furious when Carl had withdrawn a horse from Cheltenham overnight. He might have been right in saying the horse wasn't ready, but she hadn't believed that was the true reason.

Arriving at Deanly, amazingly without mishap, she was startled to find the main gates open and unguarded. With so many valuable horses in stud and in training, security had to be tight, and if her father had been here he would have immediately found who was responsible for such carelessness and sent him packing. So would Carl have done once, but now he would probably only shrug his broad shoulders. Gail clamped heavily down on her ever-growing sense of defeat as she went to find the night-watchman and told him angrily to see to his duties and that she would be reporting such criminal negligence to Mr Elliot.

Leaving the man grumbling that not even the devil himself would be out on such a night, Gail continued on her way. She had no authority to chastise the men and they knew it. It was only because they liked and respected her that they put up with it. As she was small and sensitive, without an aggressive bone in her slender body, it didn't come naturally to her to tell men often twice her size how to go about their business. Bitterness welled in her throat as she reflected how more and more she was being forced to take over Carl's role, while he sat wrapped in self-pity. She must be mad, rushing back to him like this. Even if he was in trouble, which was unlikely, she would get little thanks for it.

The big house, as the staff called it, was silent and empty. The last housekeeper had left because of Carl's temper and Gail didn't think he had advertised for another. A woman called Mavis came from the village and cleaned up, when she felt like it. At least this was the impression Gail got, taking in the general air of untidiness and neglect. Sometimes she found it difficult to believe this had once been a normal house where Carl had frequently entertained his friends, many the élite of the racing world. Gail winced as she thought of the damage Petula Hogan had done and wondered sadly how someone as intelligent as Carl could have fallen so heavily under the influence of such a worthless woman.

Her young face taut with unhappiness, she burst into his study. Normally she would have knocked, but the total silence frightened her to forgetting. At first sight it appeared her fears were not unfounded. Carl, judging by the half empty whisky bottle by his side, had been attempting to drink his way to oblivion. He was sleeping, with hot ashes from the fire he had apparently lit, smouldering dangerously on the hearthrug beside him. It might only have been a matter of minutes before the whole place was engulfed in flames!

Acting on the certain knowledge that there was no time to waste, Gail grabbed some tongs, throwing the burning coal back on the fire, then doused the still smoking carpet with what remained of the bottle of whisky. Next she caught hold of Carl's shoulder and began shaking him to his senses.

'Carl!' she cried urgently, trying to stop trembling as she realised what could have happened.

Slowly he opened his eyes, his dark face briefly unguarded. Gail's heart ached for the desolation she saw there, though she quickly controlled her betraying sympathy.

'What the hell are you doing here?' he muttered unsteadily.

'I'm not a bad dream!' she said sharply.

'No, nightmares usually disappear.'

The cruelty in his voice spoke of returning consciousness with a vengeance, but she stood her ground.

'I've probably saved your life,' she told him.

'You're becoming addicted to lost causes, you mean,' he retorted sardonically, 'and you think I'm one.'

'Nothing of the kind!' She resisted the impulse to wrap her arms round him by stiffening her voice. 'You're merely a man feeling sorry for himself.'

Furiously he glared at her. 'And you're just a woman putting her own definition on things. I'm not drunk. I was merely relaxing peacefully after a hard day—and you still haven't told me why you're back.'

Because he so clearly wished her a million miles away, she said coldly, 'It's a good job I came. The gates were unlocked and unguarded and you were in danger of being burnt to death!'

'A quick end,' he taunted indifferently. 'All my worldly goods gone as well. No more . . .'

'Misery?'

'I was about to say—interference!'

'I realise your opinion of me,' she snapped, her hands clenched, 'but someone has to try and get you back to normal.'

He rasped contemplative fingers round the stubble on chin. 'What exactly would you mean by—normal?'

Gail hesitated. He was goading her, she could see it in his eyes. She was becoming very familiar with that devilish glint. Longing to shout at him, 'Back to what you were before you met Petula Hogan!' she tightened unsteady lips. His hard glance was daring her to go as far as that!

'Why don't you find another housekeeper?' she asked weakly, instead. 'You can't go on living here alone.'

'None of them stay.'

'Since you drove Mary away.'

'I didn't!' His face became a hard, black mask. 'She deserted me when I needed her most.'

Gail sighed, wondering if he really believed it. 'You must admit, after you—you broke you leg, you were very difficult to put up with.'

'You managed.'

She could have told him why, but she didn't. It was easy to make allowances when one cared for a person. Fortunately, this time, she could find an answer without giving herself away. 'Dad asked me to keep an eye on you.'

'Night and day?'

With both his eyes and his cool voice mocking her, Gail had to take a deep breath. 'I expect it's grown to be a habit, and if I wasn't around to advise you against certain courses of action, you might soon be here entirely on your own, with no staff left at all!'

'You're all too sensitive.'

She blinked incredulously. She couldn't speak for the others, but she wouldn't like to count the number of times her ears had burned! When Carl liked, his temper was capable of blasting anyone wide open and, over the past months, he had rarely spared her because she was a girl.

'I'm sure,' she heard him continuing silkily, 'you didn't leave the Vicarage and return all the way to Deanly in order to discuss my shortcomings, or the possibility of finding another housekeeper? Unless,' he paused, blue eyes narrowed deviously, 'you're interested in the post for yourself?'

Because she was still reluctant to admit why she was here, she replied rashly, 'If we had another trainer I might be.'

'We can manage,' he said stonily.

'No, we can't, and you know it!' Lifting her chin, she stared at him calmly. 'You'll have to do something about it soon.'

It was the first time she had challenged him outright and she could tell he didn't like it. The bones of his hard handsome face tightened while his blue eyes darkened arrogantly. 'Okay,' he taunted, 'so I find a new trainer. Would you consider looking after me?'

He couldn't be serious! He knew she hadn't been and was merely amusing himself at her expense. He was teaching her to think twice before she spoke, in future. 'It wouldn't be suitable,' she said stiffly.

'Why not?'

Now he was daring her to say people would talk. Then he would reply humiliatingly that she was flattering herself in thinking that anyone would believe he was interested in a girl like her. Convinced he was inhuman, she answered helplessly, 'I—I have my reputation to think of.'

'Always guarding that, aren't we?' he jeered. 'A proper paragon of virtue, or so my men tell me. You've been wearing a chasity belt for years,' contemptuously he regarded her small, scarlet face. 'I wonder why.'

'It makes sense,' she managed, in a strangled voice.

'And for dullness,' his thin mouth twisted mockingly. 'A prim little virgin of—what? Twenty?'

'Almost twenty-two,' she gasped, 'and you don't know for sure!'

'Unless something's been going on behind the stable door no one knows about?'

She hated his horrid innuendoes. 'Nothing's been going on!'

'You're probably right. Being so plain, you'd scarcely have to put yourself in a glass case.'

Swallowing painfully, she struck out wildly. 'Perhaps all the girls you've loved and left served as a kind of warning as to what happens to those who behave indiscriminately!'

His lean body exuded boredom, though a faint colour crept under his taut jaw. 'Why don't you join your brother-in-law in his pulpit on Sundays? Within a short time I'm sure his congregation would be quite reformed.'

'It's not his congregation that needs reforming!' Gail retorted bitterly.

'You ought to use more subtlety, Miss Fenton,' he laughed.

Gail swung on her heel, her slim body stiff with resentment. She knew the futility of staying with him in his mood. He would tear her to pieces so she wouldn't get any sleep. 'See you in the morning,' she said hastily.

Apparently this didn't suit. 'Wait!' Carl commanded curtly, before she could escape. 'Now you're here, I'd like some coffee—and something to eat.'

Weakly she nodded, despising herself for giving in to him, but when he rose to his feet with a helpless limp her heart ached for him again.

While the coffee perked, she made him an omelette, stuffing it with tomatoes and mushrooms and a slice of bacon, which was all she could find. She must remember to tell him he'd better have breakfast at her place, forgetting that, lately, he usually did.

Toasting a few slices of dry bread, she loaded an attractive tray and after taking it to him left him eating while she went back for the coffee. He seemed so hungry she doubted if he had eaten all day.

He had cleared his plate when she returned and was flexing his leg, frowningly.

'Shall I rub it for you?' she asked, knowing he still suffered pain. After he had broken it he had refused to rest and it had taken longer than it might otherwise have done to heal.

'If you like,' he shrugged, portraying indifference though not outright refusal. The physiotherapist, who had been dismissed far too soon, had shown her how to do enough to give him at least some relief.

Carl hauled his jeans unselfconsciously above his knee, and for the next few minutes, trying not to tremble as she touched him, Gail massaged and kneaded. She could feel him almost visibly relax above her bent head.

'That's good,' he said suddenly, his voice not as hard as it had been.

'The coffee?' He'd had three cups.

'No, your hands.' He studied them as though he was seeing them for the first time. 'You've got beautiful hands, or didn't you realise? Perfectly shaped, with a kind of soothing magic in them.'

Her heart jerked, but she could only stare at him, never remembering him paying her a compliment before, unless it was about her riding. 'I thought you considered me plain?'

'Hmm . . .' Carl said thoughtfully, with no apology for his former disparagement. 'You're probably plain because you haven't learned to make the most of yourself. You've very fine bones and,' he sounded surprised as his glance roamed her small face, 'your eyes are extraordinary.'

'But nothing spectacular?'

'Haven't I just said they are?'

Gail might have acknowledged the delight running through her if his voice had held even a thread of interest. Already he had forgotten about her, and angrily she gave way to impulse to recover his attention.

'You don't think I'm as beautiful as Petula?'

'Shut up, damn you!' He jumped up so swiftly he almost knocked her over, but he didn't seem to notice. Unhappily, she scrambled to her own feet, feeling terribly ashamed of herself.

'I'm sorry,' she faltered, her face pale.

'Just get out, will you!' he snapped tersely, remaining with his back to her until she obliged.

Preparing for bed, Gail felt almost sick. How stupid could one get! All the time she was massaging his leg she had been burning up inside with sensation. This, and her constant sense of inexplicable frustration, must have forced Petula's name so contemptuously past her lips. In a way she was grateful for Carl's subsequent eruption which had perhaps prevented her from making an even greater fool of herself, but she still shivered from shocked reaction.

The next morning, after a restless night, she knew what she must do. To save Deanly from almost certain ruin it wasn't a housekeeper Carl needed, it was a wife! Someone close enough to him to force him to take a good long look at himself. And who would be in a better position to do this than a wife? Of course the biggest difficulty might lie in persuading him that a wife was essential in the first place. There were plenty of suitable girls in the district, but no one who could match Petula in looks. Resolutely Gail squashed down the fresh anguish in her heart, wishing, with a hint of the ridiculous which often saved her in her worst moments, that she could find a surgeon willing to remove such a painful organ completely. She would have to be clever, planting the germ of her idea discreetly, for Carl was rarely receptive to any suggestion these days. And, at the same time, if she could drop a hint that he was looking for someone to a few of the local girls who she was sure would marry him at the drop of a hat, then there might be every chance that her scheme might succeed.

She rang Ruth before breakfast, immediately she returned from the early morning gallops. 'I'm sorry about last night,' she said.

Ruth wasn't so easily appeased. 'You might remember you're my sister, my only relative. When I looked in your room and found you'd gone. I realised where you would be, but you didn't even leave a note, and it was snowing hard!'

'I'm sorry,' Gail said again. 'The snow was bad, but thank goodness it's nearly all disappeared.'

Ruth ignored this. 'Are you coming back this evening?' she wanted to know. 'Donald has a parish meeting and I'd like an excuse not to be there.'

'You're a clergyman's wife!' Gail grinned, as she grabbed the chance to rebuke Ruth, when it was so often the other way round.

'I don't see how that should make me anything less than human,' Ruth sighed. 'Sometimes I get fed up.'

'Don't we all!' Gail echoed her sister's sigh as she rang off—before Ruth had time to make her promise to return. Ruth had always been the clever one and many people, including her husband, took advantage of it. She was older and had a degree. Lady Purdie had approved of her entirely. Since their father had died, Ruth had frequently asked Gail to come and live at the Vicarage, but although there was plenty of room she always declined. She got on well with Donald and Ruth, but had no desire to share their house or their way of living.

Long ago, Gail had realised how much she loved horses and the life her father led, and, if she had no strong personal ambitions, she knew that away from the atmosphere of the racing stables she wouldn't be happy. If she couldn't have Carl—and she had never been foolish enough to imagine she could—then she would settle for a career with horses and stick to it.

Carl tried her patience sorely during the following days by disappearing to London, where he stayed for the better part of a week. He had a good assistant, quite capable of managing the stud side of the enterprise while he was away. It was the training side that was being totally neglected. When he returned and she found his temper hadn't improved, Gail decided she must have been crazy in even thinking of trying to help him. Far from attempting to find him a wife, she resolved to wash her hands of him.

Subsequently, she was disgusted to hear herself

inviting him to lunch one morning when she met him and he declared he was hungry. She felt even worse on hearing herself suggesting the very thing she had sworn not to think of again. As they sat down to eat, in the large, cosy kitchen of her father's cottage, where Carl still allowed her to live, the words seemed unhappily forced out of her. 'What you need is a wife.'

He glanced at her impatiently. 'I thought it was a housekeeper? Surely I don't need both?'

Flushing uncomfortably, she said, 'I was only joking. People feel sorry enough for you, as it is.'

There was a strange silence while his eyes narrowed. He tasted a mouthful of her delicious home-made soup, a frown on his pale, hard face.

'Is it not to your liking?'

'What?' He met her anxious gaze with a start. 'Oh, the soup? No, it's fine. You're a very good cook.'

'My grandmother taught me.'

His frown reappeared and his voice hardened. 'I don't need people feeling sorry for me. Why can't they mind their own business?'

Gail's fingers curled round her piece of French bread, crumbling it to pieces. 'You're a very difficult man to ignore.'

He had obviously never considered this. He had an arrogance which made him almost wholly indifferent to what people thought of him. A faintly hostile expression crossed his face. He didn't care for the idea of being pitied. 'Why should anyone feel sorry for me?'

Gail drew a cautious breath. 'Perhaps because you wanted Miss Hogan and she didn't want you?'

'No one can know for certain.'

She gave him a sorrowful glance which he matched with a look of anger. 'I met a girl in London while I was there. I slept with her and she had no complaints, she certainly didn't feel sorry for me.'

Flushing at such bluntness, which she suspected was deliberate because he was angry, Gail whispered miserably, 'Does this mean you've fallen in love again?'

'No,' he snarled, 'but I'm still a virile man.'

Gail didn't doubt it. One only had to look at him, but she felt so racked with pain she didn't want to. Quickly she left the table to toss a green salad and fetch the steaks which had been grilling while they ate the first course. She scorned herself for always keeping something handy in case Carl dropped in.

He had apparently been thinking while she'd been busy. 'Maybe I should get married after all,' he muttered, as she sat down beside him again.

'You mean,' Gail had never dreamt it would hurt as much and her face was white as she stared at her plate, 'the—girl in London?'

'Bettina?' A cool laugh broke from derisive lips. 'No, she would never do.'

'Then—who?'

Suddenly he gave an exasperated exclamation. 'This conversation is crazy! We must have more important things to talk about. We're running a business here, not a matrimonial agency, and all I've managed to do so far this morning is to shock your puritan little soul!'

Gail was out early the following day. There was plenty to do. Some of the older horses, coming from the roughed-off state back into racing, had to be started off with plenty of walking and trotting, the beginning of the muscle-building process, while for other horses, reaching their peak, the training had to be stepped up, with a return to the gallops in the afternoon. It was the trainer's responsibility to decide when the horses were ready to race, and both Gail and the assistant trainer missed her father greatly for this. For some of the bigger events they were forced to appeal to Carl, and his decision, these days, seemed to depend less on the horse than on the mood he was in.

Deanly was in Berkshire, the Berkshire Downs being the training ground of some of England's finest thoroughbred horses. Every day it was a common sight to see strings of them walking in single file along the roads on their way to be exercised. Gail liked the

landscape. Especially in summer, she considered the
tracks of springy turf between the huge golden
wheatfields magnificent, and in autumn and winter the
wilder countryside was windblown and bracing, with
wide views stretching to far horizons. Deanly itself lay
several miles from Lambourn, a quaint town with a
twelfth-century church and Victorian almshouses.
Many visitors came here every year to explore the
downs and, from what she had heard, few of them went
away disappointed.

After the snow, the weather had improved and the air
was crisp and fresh, with what Gail was sure was the
first touch of spring. The head lad and the racing lads
under him rode behind Gail and Frank. Gail, riding a
three-year-old colt, could keep up with the best of them,
although she didn't pretend that on the racecourse she
would have been able to compete with the jockeys who
wore Carl's colours, and often seemed to have been
born for the job rather than trained.

As they reached open country, coming to the first lap of
the gallop, she was surprised to find Carl waiting for
them. And he wasn't alone. He had company, his cousin
and several friends. Grace Elliot, Sir Arthur's daughter,
rarely rose at such an hour, and Gail's eyes widened as she
saw her approaching. Like Petula, Grace appeared to
prefer millionaires to hard-working men trying to make
an often precarious living from breeding horses. She lived
some distance from Deanly and for weeks they never saw
her, then suddenly she would turn up, as today, with some
sophisticated friends to amuse her. Gail could have
wished her a thousand miles away, that morning, as she
forced a stiff smile.

Grace, however, didn't seem to see her, all her
attention being fixed on Carl.

'Hi, cousin!' she cried, smiling, apparently artlessly.
'How are you?'

Carl, straightening from leaning against his Land
Rover, lightly kissed the cheek she tilted, undeceived by
the warmth she emanated. 'Nice to see you,' he said.

'It would be nice if you meant it,' she pouted, introducing her friends.

'How was America?' he asked, idly running his eyes over his string of horses. He didn't actually look at Gail as she stopped beside him, and she wondered if he realised she was there.

'Guess who I saw?' Grace said smugly.

'I haven't the time.'

Gail noticed him stiffen while Grace grimaced. Grace was a spoiled, only child, with a fondness for upsetting people. Gail guessed what was coming but was unable to do anything.

Helplessly she clenched her hands on her reins as she heard Grace say softly, 'I met Petula—and she didn't even ask how you were.'

Carl nodded coolly. Only Gail might have seen how pale he went. 'Did you expect her to?' He eyed his cousin cynically, then, to Gail's complete surprise, he placed his hands on her waist, something he had never done before, and lifted her out of the saddle. Putting her down by his side, he took control of her horse but kept an arm round her as if sensing she was trembling.

Grace folded her mouth in a tight little line before opening it again. 'Yes,' she said sharply, 'I did!'

Carl corrected the crooked angle of Gail's riding hat as it caught his shoulder and smoothed a heavy strand of fair hair back under it before returning his attention to Grace.

'Perhaps we've both forgotten about each other.'

His shrug was a masterpiece of carelessness, Gail thought frantically, wishing only to wriggle away from him but finding herself totally incapable of escaping his iron grasp. He was using her, she was well aware of it, though for what purpose she couldn't be sure.

Grace was staring at her with malicious suspicion which she made no attempt to conceal. 'It is possible, I suppose.'

Gail flinched. Grace's tone was both insulting and enlightening. She had swiftly jumped to the conclusion that Carl had already found someone to console him. She studied Gail closely, observing her mud-splattered face and slight body, and obviously felt convinced but incredulous. Yet there was something slightly different in her expression as she turned to leave, something Gail couldn't quite fathom.

'See you some time,' she smiled coldly at Carl over her shoulder, while her guests, with their curious glances, departed with her.

CHAPTER TWO

As soon as Grace was gone, Carl released her and turned towards the Land Rover. Terrified he was about to depart as well, Gail immediately changed the query hovering on her lips regarding his puzzling behaviour to a question about the horses.

'What about Checkers?' she asked quickly. 'Aren't you going to stay and see him run?'

'Yes,' he replied impatiently, 'if you insist.'

She could tell something had disturbed him and was annoyed with Grace for mentioning Petula. Yet if it hadn't been for Grace would she ever have known what it was like to be held in his arms? She could still feel the strength of his tall lean body and hoped he hadn't been aware of how fast her heart had been beating as he had held her close. For her it would be a moment to remember, but she guessed he had already forgotten.

She stayed by his side while the head lad put the horses through their paces. Taking off her hat, she gazed at it with awe as she recalled how Carl had straightened it. Almost reverently she put it back on again, then sighed as she realised how the dark potency of his attraction was diverting her from more important things.

'Do you think he's ready for Saturday?' she asked, referring to Checkers.

'Yes.' Carl's eyes narrowed on the horse thoughtfully. 'I'd like to see him again, this afternoon, but I think so.'

'Then we'll declare him?'

'If you must.'

Gail counted ten slowly. She didn't want to start an argument, but a horse had to be declared four days before a race as well as the day before, if he was to run. Carl's lack of enthusiasm tried her patience sorely.

The head lad rode up, expecting to be consulted,
eager to give his opinion. Frank began talking too, but
Carl had obviously lost all desire to talk about
anything. Gail recognised that look. It filled her with
dread and anger. He towered above her, her head
barely reaching his shoulder, the lean bulk of him
capable of so much both in sheer physical strength and
intelligence, she could have screamed that he could be
so deliberately obtuse.

They dispersed for breakfast, then it was more work
with the yard secretary, who was fretting over the poor
returns so far this year. There was a lot to go through,
but she was forced to agree that it was difficult to
discuss future progress when Carl didn't seem to care
whether his horses raced or not. Secretly she wondered
if Carl was thinking of giving up and sticking to
breeding, he hadn't lost so much interest in that. Gail
thought she wouldn't care what he did if only he would
make up his mind.

After lunch there was a car outside his door when she
went to see what was keeping him, and she found him
with one of Grace's beautiful friends. The girl must
have been frozen by Carl's icy demeanour earlier, but
clearly she never allowed a lack of encouragement to
deter her. She was wearing skin-tight jeans with an even
more form-fitting top which blatantly revealed every
curve of her voluptuous figure. That Carl was eyeing
her with more attention than he had paid recently to his
business made Gail's blood boil. She was sure he had
been on the point of kissing the woman when she'd
turned up, and though he didn't seem to resent Gail's
appearance, making his excuses willingly enough, she
hated the small twist of satisfaction she saw on his
mouth.

Out on the gallops, he still wouldn't finally decide
about Checkers, and she decided to leave it until that
evening. I'll cook him something nice for dinner, she
planned, hoping he might be more amiable with a good
meal inside him.

'It's very kind of you,' he said coolly, when she knocked on his study door at seven to tell him the meal was almost ready, 'but I was thinking of going out.'

'With your lunchtime visitor?'

'Don't be so astonished,' he mocked. 'I've mentioned that I still have all the usual urges.'

Gail went as pink as the shirt she was wearing. Since she had scrubbed her face twice as long as usual, the colour showed. She could have told him what to do with his urges! Staring at him morosely, she envied him his sophistication, the air of authority he must have been born with. He was amused—if anything amused him these days—by her naïvety, and she found it distressing how it pleased him to torment her.

She tried to pretend it didn't matter about the meal she had cooked so lovingly. 'You can always warm it up tomorrow,' she said. 'It needn't be wasted.'

'On the other hand, I could go out tomorrow,' he pondered aggravatingly. 'Perhaps it's a bit late to make arrangements for this evening, and your cooking is very tempting.'

Gail scowled. 'If you were so keen to go out, you only had to come to the kitchen and say so!'

'I would have done if I'd had any idea you were there,' he said smoothly.

She was certain this wasn't true, but in time she remembered she might be guilty of a little deviousness herself. She didn't usually cook Carl's dinner, and if it hadn't been for Checkers, she wouldn't have been here tonight. Easing the scowl carefully from her face, she replaced it with a smile. 'I'm sorry,' she said politely.

Leaving him with a drink, she went to set the dining-room table. Lately, she knew, he had been using the kitchen, and she didn't believe he should be allowed to forget how to be civilised altogether. Judging his mood to be mellow as they finished eating, she tackled him about the race meeting with more determination than tact.

'About Checkers on Saturday,' she began.

'You have a one-track mind,' he drawled.

'It can't be a bad thing.'

His mouth went as stubborn as hers. 'Gail, I'm no fool!' He waved a hand over the table, the remains of her delectable soufflé. 'I realise very well why you've gone to all this trouble, but I have something more important to talk about.'

'I can't think what it could be.'

'You might, in a minute.'

Impatience drove her to retort sharply, 'I'd like to bet on it!'

Carl gazed at her sternly, seeing through her uncharacteristic pertness. 'I wouldn't advise you to, young lady.'

Years ago she remembered him saying this to her, dragging her away from the tote and a dead certainty. Her angry protests had aroused considerable interest and when the horse had come in last she hadn't apologised, but she had learnt her lesson. Apart from small sums on their own horses occasionally, she never gambled.

Now, she said rather desperately, 'I suppose I can't really argue with you until I hear what you have to say, but I do know you'll have to give up racing if you don't begin taking an interest in it again soon.'

'I might try.'

He would? Over the months, all the times she had quietly pestered him, she had never got him to go as far as this. Her green eyes widened doubtfully. 'If you've had a change of heart,' she breathed, 'when did it happen?'

'Ever sceptical!' he smiled dryly. 'Perhaps since yesterday, when you proposed to me.'

Startled, she frowned. 'I said you needed a wife.'

He shrugged. 'More or less the same thing, isn't it? It was your suggestion, and you surely wouldn't want to wish anyone but yourself on a bad-tempered character like me?'

Gail's face flushed and her pulses raced, but she

refused to take him seriously. Unsteadily she said, 'I know Petula was the only woman you've ever wanted to marry, but you do need someone to help you run all this!' her expressive hands indicated the whole of Deanly. 'What you don't need is someone you feel you have to be polite to all the time.'

'I'm not always polite to the servants.'

'Those you had?'

His eyes hardened. 'You've made your point.'

'Until recently they never complained, so you must have treated them decently,' she pointed out.

'But now you believe I need a doormat?'

'It might be necessary for a while,' she kept her eyes, on the tablecloth rather than on his dark, mocking face. 'One capable of shaking off the insults you heap on them.'

Anger leapt in his glance, to be swiftly controlled, though his mouth tightened. 'How about you marrying me, Gail? I think you'd suit my present mood very well, and we do understand one another.'

You only think you understand me, she thought, not saying it aloud. Aloud she said 'You can't seriously consider marrying someone you don't love?'

'Why not?' His voice had a hard edge. 'At least I wouldn't have to pretend, and knowing how romantic the average woman is, I might have to if I married someone else.'

When Gail still hesitated, he added, 'You've lost your father, Gail, you could lose your job. In fact, refuse me and you could lose it tomorrow.'

His threats were weapons she was familiar with; it was the thought of not seeing him again she couldn't take. He believed she was being femininely coy while, in reality, she was confused. Carl never liked being thwarted, being always determined to have his own way, but she wondered if he fully realised the seriousness of what he was proposing.

As coolly as she was able, she glanced at him, hoping he didn't notice the tears in her eyes. 'If I considered it, you might expect me to let you go if Petula ever came back?'

He assured her grimly. 'She won't.'

'But—if she did?' something hurting inside Gail made her persist, as though she had an insatiable appetite for pain.

'Who knows?' he refused to be drawn. 'You know the circumstances, and a marriage can founder on many things. At least if we don't expect very much we can't be disillusioned. And if the day comes that we decide to part—well, nobody's going to be hurt.'

Gail winced. That was what he thought! But he sounded so hard and bitter she could have wept. She hadn't the heart to do anything else but give in to him. Every instinct might shriek that she was making the biggest mistake in her life, but for once she didn't listen to her intuition.

'If you think I'd be suitable,' she said humbly, 'I will marry you.'

'You aren't in love with another man?' Carl suddenly looked at her sharply, as if it had just occurred to him. 'I realise you'd sacrifice a lot for this place, but I would never ask you to go as far as that.'

'No, I'm not,' she replied tensely.

'I didn't really think you would be,' he shrugged. 'It was just a thought. In a way, being so plain, you could consider you're doing rather well for yourself, marrying me.'

Did love and hate always go hand in hand? Gail stared at him, a mixture of both in her eyes. It hurt, more than she would ever have imagined it could, that he didn't believe she was pretty enough to attract other attention. Other men had asked her out, but she didn't mention it. Anyway, it wasn't the same as being in love with someone. As for doing well for herself, she supposed in a way she would be, and plenty of people would think so, yet despite all the obvious handicaps, she was convinced she could make Carl a suitable wife. She had never been slow to learn, she didn't see why her intelligence couldn't be applied to marriage as well as other things.

Deciding to ignore his condescending remarks which, she realised resignedly, he might be surprised to learn had been hurtful, she smiled at him coolly, as if something else had been occupying her mind.

'Was this what your display of affection was leading up to, this morning?' she asked.

The withdrawn look she was coming to recognise cloaked his face. 'Lifting you from your horse could scarcely be called a display of affection.'

'I'm aware it wasn't genuine,' she told him dryly, 'but that didn't seem to be the impression you wanted to give.'

'I hope you aren't going to question every move I make,' he said coldly.

'Of course not,' she assured him, more calmly than she felt. 'We both need a certain amount of privacy.'

'Yes,' he muttered shortly, and Gail sensed he wasn't altogether pleased at the way she had framed her reply. She wasn't sure why. Her smooth brow creased with a hint of returning despair. He wasn't going to enlighten her about this morning, that much was clear! Carl wasn't used to being answerable to anyone but himself. However, she wondered unhappily, would he take to marriage?

The apprehension in her gentle green eyes, the growing paleness of her young face, brought a sudden tightening of his lips.

'Gail,' he groaned, gazing at her hard across the table, 'you do realise what you're letting yourself in for? Ours won't be an ordinary, conventional marriage, and it won't be easy. I'll probably hurt you a lot.'

It must be a step forward that he was aware that he could! Shakily she smiled, 'We'll manage.'

'You'd better think it over. Sleep on it.'

It was good advice which she might be wise to follow, but if she had the chance of saving Deanly and helping Carl, she knew she must take it. If she refused him, he might easily find another girl like Petula, and she didn't give much for his chances of surviving such an ordeal twice.

'I'd rather not think it over,' she replied slowly, 'unless you feel you've been too impulsive yourself?'

'I don't doubt it,' he said dryly. 'I must be out of my mind, asking an innocent young girl like you to share my life, but I feel exactly as you do.'

Gail nodded and tried to smile, hoping he didn't notice the unhappiness in her eyes. But although he was looking at her, he didn't seem to be really seeing her. He was preoccupied and remote, his face gaunt and strained, betraying that it wasn't herself he was thinking of.

With an effort she kept her underlying bitterness under control. It was no use thinking that if Carl's had been a normal proposal, she might have been in his arms. Sternly she reminded herself that there would be no kisses for her, apart from perhaps odd brotherly ones, and she would be foolish to expect anything more.

The small jerk Carl gave confirmed that his thoughts had been elsewhere, but, as she regained his attention, his mouth did relax slightly. 'I'll take you home, Gail. No, leave the dishes!' he commanded firmly, as she began gathering them up. 'I'll get Mavis to see to them in the morning.' Before he left her at her door, he said, 'You can leave everything to me, I'll make all the necessary arrangements. I think we should be married as soon as possible.'

Ruth was startled when Gail rang the following evening, with her news. Carl was going ahead so quickly with plans for an early wedding, Gail thought she should tell Ruth before she heard it from someone else.

'I had no idea you were even very friendly!' Ruth exclaimed, always frank. 'I mean, only a few months ago Mr Elliot—Carl—was crazy over that Hogan woman, wasn't he? I remember Dad telling me about it.'

'Petula married someone else.' Gail explained.

'And now he's going to, which proves he's as changeable. He could as easily get tired of you.'

'He won't.' Gail didn't mention that as Carl wasn't in love with her she was in no danger of being let down, at least not in the way Ruth imagined.

'You're in love with him,' Ruth went on, making Gail gasp, 'but what about Carl? Are you sure he's not just using you?'

It was so near the truth Gail almost gasped again while she had to pretend to be bewildered. 'Using me?' she queried.

Ruth snorted. 'Well, you adore him and won't make him a bad wife, and there can't be much you don't know about horses. Dad used to say you were nearly as good as he was, and Carl Elliot's no fool. Marrying you could save him going to the expense of a new trainer, which must be a consideration when he hasn't been doing much lately.'

As Ruth was just being Ruth, Gail felt no real resentment and was dismayed to hear herself asking, 'You don't think my appearance could have anything to do with it?'

To her horror, Ruth's pause indicated that she was taking her sarcastic remark seriously. 'Well, you aren't exactly a beauty, darling. Your hair and skin's good and your nose is straight, but you neglect yourself terribly . . .'

'I never have much time.' Gail didn't know why she should leap to her own defence when she had never been very interested in how she looked.

'I think you've been a long time in growing up,' Ruth replied enigmatically.

'Anyway,' Gail made an effort to brighten the conversation, 'Carl wants us to get married soon, so he's coming over. He would like to see you.' She didn't say she had insisted and that Carl had been furious. Putting down the phone, she still winced at his words. 'I'm marrying you, Gail, and it's a business proposition,' nothing, I'm sure, to be blessed in church! We can be married quietly in a register office. I don't know about you, but I can do without being gaped at by innumerable guests and having your dear brother-in-law gabbling sanctimoniously over me!'

'His name is Donald,' she'd said mutinously, 'and he doesn't gabble!'

They had quarrelled fiercely, but as it wasn't the first time and certainly wouldn't be the last, she had managed not to be too upset. Carl was arrogant and overbearing, while she guessed he was right in saying that her father had allowed her a little too much of her own way, In the end, when they had both capitulated a little, Carl had remarked that it must be a good sign.

He decided they would be married immediately, without announcing it to the world until it was over. Although he wouldn't hear of a white wedding, he did eventually agree to being married in church, but with a special licence and only a few close friends.

In a hurry, Gail found a short dress and jacket which looked very nice, but she realised, as she put it on before the ceremony, that it did nothing for her. She sighed for the half-formed dreams she had had of gleaming satin and lace, with a long flowing veil, thrown back after she became Carl's wife to reveal— with the help of the local beauty salon—a face transformed almost beyond recognition. All she had had time for was to have her hair washed and set, an effort which to her seemed dismally wasted as the thick, lustrous strands of it were crushed under her hat. They'd been busy right up until the last moment, with the horses they had had entered for Chepstow winning, and two others, for Epsom, hard in training. With so much to do, Gail hadn't had much chance to worry over her appearance, and, gazing at herself before she set off for church, she thought perhaps it was just as well. She looked far too young and inexperienced to be the bride of a man like Carl Elliot.

Carl, in a dark suit and pale shirt, was a tall

impressive figure. Like herself, he might have dressed
swiftly, but the result was vastly different. His cool,
detached appearance was enviable when her own limbs
trembled and the remote glance he bent on her as she
paused by his side was something she might have given
anything to achieve.

Soon after they had decided to get married, Carl had
declared they would return to Deanly immediately after
the ceremony, He had changed his mind only when Gail
had remarked how his aristocratic relations might be
horrified if there wasn't a reception afterwards.

'There won't be enough of them to make a fuss,' he
had grunted.

'The few you've asked all live locally,' Gail had
reminded him, 'and I'd rather not have them accusing
me of inciting you to meanness already. They'd be
glaring down their noses at me every time we met.'

'Let them,' he had replied indifferently, but eventually
he had given in. Swinging, she thought, too far in the
other direction, he had ordered an extravagant
luncheon in a five-star hotel.

She had argued futilely over the paying for it. 'The
reception is the bride's responsibility,' she had
protested, flushing as she said bride, sure that no girl
could ever have felt less like one.

'Not any more, and definitely not this time,' Carl had
retorted so grimly she had been silenced. 'Your father
didn't leave a great deal of money, and what you have
you must keep. You might need it for something more
important.'

Such as if they parted? He didn't actually say so, but
she was sure that was what he was thinking? 'Very well,'
she had sighed, reflecting that there could be some sense
in what he was hinting.

They left the church in Carl's car, driven by one of his
men. He had refused to ride in the conventional saloon
decked out with white ribbons. Sir Arthur Elliot
bristling with disapproval, followed in his Rolls. He was
a great man for doing things properly, and even though

Carl had let it be known that the wedding would be quiet because of Gail's recent bereavement, he considered Carl's family the more important. If he'd had any say in the matter—which he hadn't!—the wedding of his only nephew would have been quite a different affair.

Carl's cousin Grace was there too, one person Gail felt she could have done without. They had met while she had been shopping for her wedding dress and Grace had manoeuvred herself in front of her so she'd been forced to stop.

'Are you being married in white?' Grace had asked after the briefest of greetings, her disparaging glance seeming to question Gail's right to be.

'Er—not exactly. I've chosen cream,' Gail had stammered uncomfortably.

Grace had fixed her gaze on the chain store bag Gail was carrying. 'Perhaps I could help you?' she had volunteered, obviously unable to believe the evidence of her own eyes. 'I know just the place where you can get a super dress.'

Gail wished now she had ignored Carl's stipulations and her own pride and thrown the chain store dress, good value that it undoubtedly was, in the nearest waste bin. If she had allowed Grace to help her, Carl might have been looking at her, at this moment, instead of out of the car window.

Tentatively she touched his arm, somewhat alarmed by his haggard face. 'How do you feel?'

'For God's sake!' he snapped, 'I'm not an invalid. All I feel is regret, which isn't exactly a crippling disease.'

It could be, as Gail was learning to her cost, but she felt now wasn't the time to discuss it. 'I thought the church looked very nice,' she said hollowly, throwing a warning glance at the driver. Carl had lowered his voice, but the bitterness in it might have carried. 'Ruth made a wonderful job of the flowers.'

'Yes,' Carl took the hint. 'Remind me to thank her.'

She turned to him a small, anxious face. 'The few people we invited seemed lost.'

He said impatiently, 'I don't suppose they felt it.'

With a sharp catch of her breath, Gail took off her hat. Her hair, freed from its confining restraint, tumbled forward over her cheeks and a shimmer of tears gave her a brief, transient beauty. 'I wish Dad could have been here,' she sighed.

He nodded, then frowned, as if something about her, rather than what she was saying, disturbed him. His glance softened suddenly on her tear-damp cheeks and tremulous lips. 'Gail?' he began, then paused abruptly, as though refusing to succumb to the appeal of her vulnerable young face.

'Yes?' she whispered faintly.

'I was merely wondering,' he said shortly, 'where you'd bought your dress.'

The implied criticism brought a surge of humiliation. 'I like it,' she replied defiantly, refusing to confess that she didn't.

'It's not too bad,' he agreed, after another pause, and she wondered wryly if such a remark was meant to save her feelings. 'You might have done better,' he added, 'if you'd taken Ruth, or even Grace, with you. Grace is a bitch, but she does have impeccable dress sense.'

'Perhaps you should blame yourself, not me!' Gail retorted, envying the other girl even his back-handed compliment. 'You told me to get anything.'

'I've never noticed you being so willing to follow my advice before.'

'Well, does it matter?' she asked crossly.

She was surprised when he considered this with a frown. 'I think it does. If I have a dowdy wife, people are going to feel sorrier for me than ever. Don't get me wrong, it's not something I intend losing sleep over, but I hate sympathy.'

Gail bit her lip unhappily. If Carl said she was dowdy then she must be. He knew too much about women not to know what he was talking about. 'You knew what I was like when you asked me to marry you,' she pointed out.

'I don't believe I ever took a good look,' he said curtly. 'I know how you work, how you think, but somehow your appearance never occurred to me.'

Gail didn't doubt for a moment that this was true. Over the years, often for days on end, she had worked with him in the stables, and while she was aware that he admired her skill with horses, she didn't believe he had ever seen her as a woman. And certainly not as a woman to be taken out and made love to.

Clenching her hands against the hurt of his words, as she realised the regrettable truth of them, she vowed not to lose her temper. Quietly she asked, 'If you think I'm dowdy, what do you suggest I do about it?'

'Get yourself a few smarter clothes, I suppose.' His mouth twisted, as though the subject already bored him. 'Whatever it is women do to transform themselves from plain Janes into raving beauties.'

And how would he treat her then, if, for her, such a transformation was possible? Gail choked back a gurgle of unhappy laughter. He was so used to her as she was now, she doubted if he would ever see her any differently, no matter what she did. 'I can try,' she conceded, 'but I can't guarantee success. You'll have to be patient.'

'Oh, forget it,' he retorted irritably. 'This is a crazy conversation.'

Gail thought it must be one of the strangest, between a husband and wife not married an hour! Out of the corner of her eye she saw Carl relax in his corner, his face set in lines of black retrospection. She reminded herself that it had been her own remarks which must have given him the idea of getting married in the first place, so she had only herself to blame if she was unhappy. She could have refused, but when he had proposed, she hadn't been thinking of herself so much as of Deanly and him. It jolted her to realise how, at this early stage, she was already beginning to wonder if she hadn't made a terrible mistake.

During the reception, as she did her best to pretend

to be a happy bride, it surprised her that Carl appeared
to be making a similar effort. He put an arm round her
as they waited to receive their guests, and when Sir
Arthur, restored to humour by several glasses of vintage
champagne, asked if it wasn't about time he kissed the
bride, he obliged with a convincing degree of
willingness.

As Gail raised her face with fleeting apprehension
instinctively to meet his descending mouth, she wasn't
prepared for the high-voltage feeling which shot
through her as their lips met. It was the first time Carl
had kissed her, or she might have been prepared. She
felt wildly indignant that, knowing this, he didn't spare
her. He must have heard the muffled exclamation that
parted her startled lips, but instead of showing
consideration the pressure of his mouth immediately
hardened and he continued kissing her until she gasped
for breath.

When he raised his head, her eyes were dilated like
someone in shock, but Carl's attention was on his
uncle, his voice sardonic as he asked if he was satisfied.
Gail might have squirmed, as Sir Arthur consumed
more champagne and his remarks grew even more
suggestive, if she hadn't been almost wholly absorbed
by the sensations that still lingered from Carl's kisses.
Her mind seemed completely disorganised, while her
body was consumed by a peculiar weakness. Even her
hands trembled for a long time afterwards, forcing her
to conceal them in her lap as they sat down to lunch,
for fear anyone noticed.

Carl, extremely observant, became aware that she
wasn't as calm as she would have liked to have been.
'I'm sorry if my obliging Arthur upset you,' he
murmured, taking his place beside her.

'I'm not upset,' she denied, lowering wavering green
eyes. 'If I am, it's just nerves.'

'Your hands are shaking.'

'No, they're not!' She hated the mockery in his voice.

'Then why hide them?'

Defiantly she placed them on the table.

'That's better!' He picked up her left one which was nearest to him, a twist of satisfaction on his hard mouth. 'I must admit I couldn't have found a bride with lovelier hands. They certainly justify what I spent on your rings.'

Gail had worked hard on her hands over the past two weeks, and though she had always taken what she sometimes thought of as ridiculous care of them, they had improved. On her long pale, incredibly slender fingers, her engagement ring glittered beside the wedding ring Carl had placed there not so long ago. Suddenly she felt panic-stricken as she realised exactly what those rings meant, and it showed in her face.

Again noticing her distress, Carl returned mockingly to what he believed was bothering her. 'That surely wasn't the first time you've been kissed?'

'No . . .'

Before she could explain, or try to, the few dates she had made, the odd kiss, which had left her cold, Carl jumped grimly to the wrong conclusion.

'So you mightn't be as innocent as you seem? I thought not, by the way you responded to me.'

While he was wrong in doubting her innocence, she couldn't deny her own response. She had responded to him, or rather her body had. It was her mind that had been protesting, fearing ravishment.

The first gleam of interest she had seen all day entered his eyes, but it was mixed with disparagement. 'None of us can help how we feel, Gail. I imagine we're all much the same underneath, whatever the packaging. But as long as you're my wife you must be sure to keep your feelings under control. I won't tolerate you finding another man to help you relieve them. You'd be well advised to channel all your rampant energy into looking after Deanly and me. Until I get tired of you.'

In a way Gail was grateful for Carl's contemptuous remarks. She was so incensed, she was able to forget how much she loved him, and for the rest of the afternoon the anger inside her converged in a wit which, if not exactly brilliant, was entertaining enough to make people murmur with surprise that Carl might have done better for himself than they had first imagined. Seeing the approval in their eyes, Gail tried to appreciate it, but she knew she would have exchanged every bit of her so-called intelligence for even a fraction of such beauty as Petula had!

They weren't going away for a honeymoon. Having so many race meetings to attend during the coming weeks provided a reasonable excuse, and they were able to pretend easily that they would have one later in the year. As soon as they arrived home, Carl changed and went out, saying he would be in later for dinner.

It all seemed a bit of an anticlimax. They had talked about a honeymoon but agreed it wasn't a good idea. Gail suspected she had been against it even more than Carl. He had offered to take her abroad, providing they could find some place where there was plenty to do so they wouldn't be bored. This, presenting a depressing picture of a busy resort with Carl disappearing each evening in the company of some glamorous female, had made Gail shudder. She had refused, pointing out hastily that as theirs wasn't to be a proper marriage, a honeymoon would be pointless. Yet despite this, she had known a quiver of regret when Carl agreed. Now she rather wished they had gone away, for suddenly she didn't think it could have been any worse than staying at home.

She was still wandering aimlessly round the house when he returned at six, but when she heard him coming she rushed to put the kettle on. She didn't really want a cup of tea, but making one would give her something to do.

It didn't apparently hide her agitation, though. 'Not having second thoughts already?' Carl asked curtly, pausing in the kitchen door, observing her tense face.

'It would be a bit late . . .'

Suddenly the kettle was whipped from her hands.

'Far too late!' he rasped, his hot glance scorching her. 'I won't be let down twice!'

'I promised you I wouldn't let you down,' she said feverishly. 'What must I do to convince you?'

He retorted savagely, 'Try not giving the clear impression that you want to escape—that you regret marrying me!'

Gail flinched as his hands clamped on her shoulders. She supposed there was some truth in his accusations. She had been feeling rather desperate and it must have shown, but she certainly wasn't thinking of running away!

'I'm sorry,' she whispered, as always feeling a need to pacify him, stronger than anger. 'Leaving you is the last thing I would do, and I thought you would have realised.'

CHAPTER THREE

CARL continued staring down at her and she couldn't tell whether he believed her or not. He had the kind of face which frequently concealed his feelings.

Finally he said, 'Perhaps it wouldn't be a bad thing if you did leave me. I didn't realise that after marrying you I might be pitied even more than I was.'

'Because I'm plain?'

'You can say that again!'

'Looks aren't everything!' she retorted wearily, wishing she had never mentioned the word pity to him, ever!

'If you tell me often enough,' he grated, 'you might begin to convince me.'

Twin flags of colour scorched Gail's cheeks, yet she refused to be defeated by his disdain. She was well aware that he was thinking of Petula and what might have been. He was merely hitting out against the bad deal he considered fate had dealt him. He needed a scapegoat and his wife was filling the role nicely. It mightn't be until all the poison of his ill-fated romance was out of his system that he would begin to recover. Until he did, Gail knew she must try and ignore the hurtful things he said to her, even if meant growing a thicker skin!

Over-brightly, she said, 'At least your guests at the wedding didn't think I was dumb!'

'Because you know all about racing.'

Her brow creased. He was right, of course. She flushed again with humiliation. 'Please switch on the kettle,' she begged, knowing she couldn't let him continue mocking her like this and keep her cool. 'I'm longing for a cup of tea.'

'Why don't you go and change while I make one?'

41

Carl suggested wryly. 'I don't think I can bear to look at you much longer in that dress.'

Because his unexpected quirk of humour made her feel suddenly better, she laughed. 'I forgot I had it on.'

'Which proves you're no more impressed by it than I am.'

'I'm sorry,' she gazed down at it ruefully, 'I ought to have given it more thought.'

'Let's forget about it,' he propoosed magnanimously. 'Run along.'

Obeying him with a sigh of relief, Gail halted just as she turned. 'I knew I'd have to move in here,' she said awkwardly, 'but you haven't told me where I'm to sleep.'

'Naturally you'll be sleeping with me,' he said curtly.

Gail felt a quiver running through her. He couldn't mean it! Hadn't he hinted several times that they wouldn't have that kind of marriage? Sharply she brought a halt to her tumutuous thoughts. 'I can't,' she said starkly.

'You can and you will.' Carl met her apprehensive eyes without a flicker of sympathy. 'At the moment we have no servants, but we'll be getting some soon, and I won't have them speculating about us, understand?'

'I'm sure they wouldn't,' she protested weakly.

Derisively his brows rose, then he appeared to take pity on her. 'When I say you sleep with me, I don't mean we have to share the same bed. I've had a single one moved into my room, which should be enough to prevent any gossip.'

In this instance, she didn't care what people thought. What she did care about was her own feelings. Sharing the same room, even in separate beds, spoke of an intimacy she hadn't been prepared for. Yet Carl made it sound so reasonable she was at loss for words. She could only manage to repeat, like someone in shock, 'I can't!'

'Don't be foolish,' he frowned, as if he was speaking to a child. 'Come, I'll show you. I would have had to, anyway, as I don't suppose you've been upstairs before.'

As she blindly tried to resist, he hauled her beside him up the stairs. Striding along a broad corridor, he flung open the door of his room. 'There,' his breathing was unaltered while she panted, 'what do you think?'

Her dazed glance wandered over the large suite. The two beds stood in the middle of it, against the far wall. There was plenty of space, she had to admit. She couldn't complain that they would be cramped, not in a room the size of this!

Helplessly she nodded, conscious that he was still holding her arm, with his breath like a caress on her warm forehead. 'It—it looks very nice.'

He showed her the bathroom, already taking her capitulation for granted. 'I'll leave you to freshen up,' he said. 'I could do with a shower myself, but I can wait.'

'My clothes are still at the cottage,' she remembered suddenly. Carl had told her to bring them over, but she had been reluctant to move in before they were married. She had felt, as well, that to do so would be like saying goodbye for ever to the carefree life she had shared with her father. She didn't want to think of her father. Although he would have been pleased that she had married Carl, the nature of their marriage might have dismayed him.

Carl didn't seem bothered by her confession. 'It doesn't matter,' he said. 'I'll take you over later and you can get a few things. The rest can wait until tomorrow. We'll just have to put up with that dress a little longer, but you can always wash your hands.' Releasing her arm, he glanced at her enigmatically. 'Come down when you're ready, I'll make some tea.'

They went in Carl's car to the cottage. 'You look too tired to walk,' he said, 'and my leg doesn't feel so good either.'

'I'll rub it for you,' Gail volunteered.

'I'll take a couple of pills,' he retorted shortly. 'You

don't have to offer your services every time I complain.'

Gail said goodbye to the cottage secretly, disguising her distress. She had spent the previous night at the Vicarage with Ruth and Donald, but now she felt she was leaving for good. When they returned again, to what was now her new home, she hurried straight upstairs to shed a few tears as she changed into a skirt and blouse.

Carl's wry glance, as she entered the study, where he was reading some letters, seemed to confirm the impression she had received on catching a glimpse of herself in a mirror before coming down. She didn't look very glamorous for a bride on her wedding night. Inwardly she sighed. Disregarding the fact that she wasn't really a proper bride, both she and Carl would have to put up with her present wardrobe until she had time to replace it with something better.

'We have to discuss staff,' Carl grimaced, as they washed up after a makeshift dinner consisting of soup, scrambled eggs and cheese. He had offered to take her out for dinner, but suddenly, the thought of having to wear her one shabby evening dress had been more than she could bear.

'Couldn't we leave it until tomorrow?' she begged.

'I suppose so,' he conceded doubtfully. 'You've enough to do without taking over here, though.'

'What makes you think I'll do that?' She began automatically polishing glasses.

'I recognised a certain look in your eye when you spotted some cobwebs,' he grinned.

'I'll look the other way,' she promised, so enchanted by his smile she was ready to promise him anything. When he forgot Petula and was pleasant, she was reminded wistfully of how he used to be.

'It's not late, but you've had a long day.' He took the tea-towel firmly from her hands, slinging it over the rail of the cooker. 'I think you ought to go to bed.'

She was about to argue, then suddenly gave in. 'It

might be a good idea,' she acknowledged, trying to look composed as she wished him a cool goodnight. He made no attempt to kiss her and she didn't expect it. He had kissed her at the reception, but after his uncle's remarks it would have looked odd if he hadn't. As she left him in the hall she was aware of both relief and disappointment. If Carl had kissed her now, she might have found herself clinging to him, begging him to make love to her, which would never do, not when he was still in love with Petula.

For all she was tired, it was a long time before Gail fell asleep. She showered and put on her pyjamas, thinking, with a slightly shamed flush, that she looked better without them. Her body was slender, well formed and firm from the exercise she took. She tried to see herself through Carl's eyes and failed. He made no secret of his opinion of her with her clothes on, she didn't think if would make any difference if he saw her with them off.

Her face hot, she crept into her single bed, her eyes fixed apprehensively on Carl's larger one. Would it comfort him if she gave herself to him? He made no secret of the fact that he was a very virile man. And if she proved satisfactory in bed he might even learn to love her. In time he might eventually forget how badly Petula had deceived him. On the other hand, Gail pondered anxiously, if she failed to please him he could despise her more than he did now. Tempting him to make love to her might not be worth the risk, just supposing she had known how to set about it.

In the end, exhaustion removed the responsibility of such a decision from her, and she was fast asleep when Carl came to bed. She slept dreamlessly all night and when she woke at six he was gone, his sheets scarcely disturbed.

After dressing hastily, she ran downstairs to discover he hadn't been in bed at all. He had been preparing for it when his manager had called. One of their most valuable mares had dropped her foal prematurely, in the early morning, with complications. The vet was there, and when Gail walked into the kitchen and Carl told her what had happened, she offered to make them both breakfast.

He accepted, though not with noticeable gratitude. He merely nodded and asked belatedly if she had slept well. She fancied she saw a flicker of mockery in his eyes as she said she had, but she didn't look at him long enough to make sure.

He was tired, she could see, but even so, he was still a powerful, imposing man. His dark head was set arrogantly on broad shoulders and the smell of horses and sweat assaulted her nostrils in a sensuous wave. As his blue eyes raked over her, her breathing altered, nearly deafening her. Suddenly she realised how much she loved him and, with a sense of chilling shock, just how vulnerable she was.

As if tiredness made him forget everything but the present moment, he took a quick step towards her. Something about her trembling young body might have quickened a chord of response in him, for a muscle at the side of his hard mouth jerked while his eyes darkened.

In a daze, Gail felt his hands close over her slender arms. 'Why don't we forget breakfast,' he muttered huskily, 'and go upstairs?'

Gail didn't know how she might have answered if the vet hadn't knocked on the door. As Carl stepped back and curtly bade the man enter, she hastily grabbed the frying pan, hoping such apparent activity might explain her burning cheeks. The incident which had just occurred confused her, but she realised instantly, from the expression on his face, that Carl regretted it almost as soon as he had touched her. The dislike in his eyes was so obvious, she prayed the vet wouldn't notice.

After cooking the plates of bacon and eggs, she drank a cup of coffee, then left to begin clearing out her father's cottage. This, along with her work in the stables, kept her busily occupied during the following days. It was the same old pattern, she reflected soberly, one morning; nothing had really changed. Carl still concentrated almost solely on the breeding side of things, while she did her best to cope with the other. He still refused to discuss a new trainer, but he did begin talking to her more, although it wasn't until the end of their third week together that she realised it.

Since Petula had gone and her father had died, Gail had found it almost impossible to have a rational conversation with him. Months ago she had given up seeking his advice about anything, even wringing a decision from him had proved exhausting. Now, slowly, this order of things appeared to be changing. She wasn't sure if he was conscious of it himself, but he frequently began discussing something on the estate, and, if a crisis arose, he might be terse, but he wasn't above asking her opinion. Over dinner he liked to talk about racing and sales. She was learning a lot about the various blood-lines of his thoroughbred stock and felt grateful that she could ask intelligent questions. It was the personal side of their relationship which remained stagnant. After the first morning he had kept his distance. They might share a room, but he never came near her.

One Monday he surprised her by saying, 'You must need a bit of a break, you're always working. Why not come to London with me? I'm going tomorrow for a couple of days.'

'To London?'

'Yes,' his mouth twisted wryly. 'Don't look so surprised, I used to go regularly.'

'Before we were married.'

'Well, yes,' reading her uncertain thoughts clearly, he shrugged, 'those days are past. This time I'm only going on business and to see my solicitor. You could shop, or whatever it is women do in town. I thought it would be a change for you.'

That he considered her at all made Gail breathless. She had been busy lately, especially as they hadn't yet found a housekeeper. Her green eyes began sparkling in anticipation. Ruth had gone to a university in London, but all she had ever managed were odd days. Not that cities appealed to her much, not even capitals, but she suddenly knew it would be different being there with Carl. 'I'd love to!' she smiled at him radiantly. 'As you say, it will make a nice change.'

Later that same day, she went over the yard to consult him about something. With his manager, he shared a different office from the one his trainer used. He had a different secretary too, one who came daily.

Outside the office door, Gail paused to tighten her shoe lace and was just in time to hear Carl telling Mrs Reed that he was taking his wife to London for two days and asking her to make the necessary arrangements.

'The usual hotel?' Mrs Reed asked quickly.

'Yes——' Carl paused suddenly, then said tersely, 'Yes, I suppose so. Although perhaps you should book a suite instead of just a room.'

Gail crept away, her face burning with humiliation. Carl didn't have his own apartment. He usually stayed in a world-famous hotel, and she realised clearly why he had hesitated so conspicuously. He was doubtful as to whether she would fit in,

She still felt scorched by shame as she sat in the car beside him the following morning. She could see she had only herself to blame that his opinion of her appearance was so low. Apart from immediately after they were married, she hadn't given it another thought. Now she bitterly regretted the weeks she had lost, and hoped it wasn't too late. Suddenly, overnight, she seemed to have grown up and was beginning realise there was more to life than hard work and horses!

While she would never pretend she could be beautiful, she knew there was a lot of room for improvement. She had clung to her careless appearance, using it like an unconscious defence, rather than because she was fond of it. She had seen Carl with beautiful girls, both before and after Petula, and everything inside her had rebelled against perhaps being used as he had used them. She hadn't stopped to consider that, as his wife, she was in quite a different position, much stronger than theirs had been, and that she could only consolidate it by improving herself. This way, she stood a good chance of earning at least his respect and affection, something which might compensate in some measure for not having his love.

She asked Carl to drop her off in the West End, before they reached their hotel. He agreed, his only stipulation being that she didn't get lost. He would see her later, he said, giving her an abstracted wave.

The previous afternoon Gail had rang Ruth, asking about London beauty salons. Ruth had been able to recommend a famous one where, by sheer chance, Gail had been fortunate enough to get an appointment because of a cancellation. The salon was able to give her only a few hours, but she came away thinking it worth every penny she had spent.

It wasn't cheap, but the advice and treatment she received was invaluable. They had removed every trace of her amateurishly applied make-up and later given her lessons on how to apply it properly. But before this they examined her skin, instructing her how to cleanse and moisturise it thoroughly. She had a good skin, she was told, Its slightly roughened appearance had been caused by cold winds and neglect, but at her age such damage was easily corrected. After various treatments, Gail was amazed at the difference. Her skin was smooth and pale with an almost translucent glow. Never in her wildest dreams had she imagined she could look as good as this.

Before she left they did her hair. It was five weeks since she had had it trimmed. Now it was cut again, but so cleverly that when it was washed and blown dry it waved about her small head so beautifully that Gail was entranced.

'Come and visit us every few months,' the beautician smiled as Gail thanked her, 'and use the creams we've

given you in between. Then you need never look the
way you did again.'

Gail, already feeling a different person, had a quick
cup of coffee and a sandwich for lunch, then went
shopping for clothes. She hadn't much time, it was
almost three o'clock, but again following Ruth's
recommendation she found a West End store and a
saleswoman who helped her enormously. With her aid,
Gail chose three evening dresses and a velvet cloak
along with various other outfits for day time wear as
well as handbags and shoes. She had spent far too
much, she thought, arriving laden at the hotel. Having
discarded the tweed coat she had been wearing in
favour of a casual but smart two-piece, she wondered if
Carl would recognise her.

He hadn't returned yet, she discovered, on being shown
to their suite. She felt an absurd disappointment. She had
meant to make an entrance and expected he would be
there to receive her. Like royalty, she supposed, quelling a
despairing giggle. She tried to convince herself she had no
need to worry. The young man who had carried her
parcels from the taxi kept glancing at her with admiration
in his eyes, which convinced her she must be looking a lot
better than she had done.

She checked at reception to see if there was a message
for her, but as there wasn't she assumed that Carl must
still be engaged with his business. Again feeling
wickedly extravagant, she orderd tea to be brought to
the suite. She could have had it in one of the lounges,
but didn't care for the idea of having it there alone.
Afterwards, as it was six o'clock and Carl still hadn't
turned up, she thought she would have a wander and
see if there was any sign of him. She felt strangely
restless and knew she wouldn't settle until he arrived.

It must have been sheer chance that when passing one
of the lounges, she should turn her head and spot him
having tea with an attractive blonde. She seemed
strangely familiar and Gail recognised her as the friend
of Grace's who had come to see him at Deanly.

Bitterly Gail observed how Carl appeared to be enjoying himself. Her wounded stare must have alerted him, for he looked up. Murmuring something to his companion, he rose, winding his way over the room towards where Gail was standing.

As he reached her, he asked, 'Have you had tea?'

The abruptness of his question was disconcerting, but she managed to nod.

Gazing at her keenly, he seemed more interested in her expression than how she looked. 'Come and meet Felicity. You remember?—Grace's friend.'

'I'd rather not,' Gail said quickly.

'Just as you like.'

He was as cold as she was, but he objected to what he clearly considered was her unreasonable attitude, while she was merely hurt that he should desert her for another girl.

Angrily she lifted her chin. 'How long will you be?'

Again he didn't appear to like her manner. 'I can't say.'

With that, Gail was forced to be content, if not happy. Retracing her steps, she felt so miserable she wished she had never come. So much for her high hopes—if they had been mixed with apprehension. Carl's attention had already wandered; he had never even noticed his wife's improved appearance!

The suite had two bedrooms. Choosing one of them, Gail flopped down before a mirror. She looked like a beautiful, wholesome child, with an air of vitality, certainly, but with none of the exciting, sexy, undertones which seemed necessary to keep a man chained to a woman's side. She frowned. She could never be that possessive, but she would give anything to have Carl so in love with her he would want to be beside her all the time.

Gail's frown deepened as she considered her height. Five foot three! She wasn't tall enough to make an immediate impact, as Petula was able to. Petula, at just under six feet, attracted attention without even trying and her statuesque beauty drew eyes like a magnet. Her dark, distinctive appearance and regal bearing made much better looking girls than Gail fade into insignificance. And now Carl had found this other girl, Felicity, and it didn't take a second glance to see what she had going for her! Grinding her small white teeth, Gail felt she could have burst into tears.

After Carl's indifferent glance, which had seemed not to see her, all she felt she had left was her fighting spirit. There seemed no obvious answer to the problems that beset her, but never having been used to giving up easily, she resolved to give her new image one more chance. Sometimes men were blind, frequently she wasn't too observant herself if she was thinking of other things. Carl might have been feeling guilty, torn between a sense of duty and his natural inclinations. The next time they met he might take a really good look at her and be impressed.

After listening for him coming upstairs, she popped into her bathroom and turned on the shower. He came to her room, apparently making sure she was there, then she heard the door of his own room open and close. As she left the shower she could hear him having one, through the wall, and guessed that, like herself, he would be changing for the evening. Unless she tarried too long, he wouldn't come to her room again.

She had difficulty in deciding which of her new dresses to wear. Finally she settled for the silvery green as the soft, feminine lines gave a deceptive fragility to her appearance. The dress was lovely, but she paid more attention to her make-up, trying to apply it exactly as she had been taught by the beautician. She might not have managed too expertly, but she wasn't dissatisfied with the results. The foundation gave an extra glow to her skin and she darkened her lashes with mascara before moistening her lips with gloss. The finished effect, when her hair was done, was good. Going to the lounge, she waited nervously for Carl to appear.

Carl's dark evening attire fitted him so perfectly he took her breath away. As always, she found it difficult to believe that this impressive-looking man, with his tall, powerful body and easy self-assurance, was her husband.

Because she noticed everything about him in a moment, she knew a sense of defeat when he merely congratulated her on her new dress.

'It suits you,' he said, his eyes barely touching her.

'I'm glad you like it,' she clenched her hands, 'I spent quite a lot of money.' She thought that might impress him, but it didn't.

'Good.' It was like water off a duck's back, as Sean's old mother used to say. 'I hope you enjoyed yourself?'

'In a way.'

He glanced at her, one dark brow slightly raised, only concerned by the droop of her wide, soft mouth, mistaking the reason for it. 'I hope you weren't too upset, finding me downstairs with Felicity?'

His query so clearly held a hint of apology that she had to assure him she wasn't. 'I think I was suffering more from reaction than anything else. You know how it is. I came up here, expecting to find you, and you weren't anywhere to be seen. And—well,' she smiled at him ruefully, 'I'm afraid I'm not used to big cities, I imagined all sorts of things might have happened to you . . .'

'Yes,' he interrupted, gently for him, 'I can see how it might have been, and I'm sorry. You might not believe it, but I was actually looking for you when I bumped into Felicity, who claimed she was waiting for a friend. Personally I think she was just looking for any fool willing to give her tea and attention, and when I hoped you might rescue me, you refused.'

Gail sighed for her own hastiness. 'I didn't understand.'

'Forgive me?'

She was so grateful that he wasn't apparently enamoured with Felicity that she was quite willing to.

She wasn't so sure she could forgive him not noticing
her changed appearance, but, she reminded herself, she
must give him time. At least his self-consciousness must
have registered something, for he didn't glance at her
doubtfully when he suggested they had dinner downstairs.

'I managed to get a couple of tickets for a show,' he
confessed, as they walked into one of the restaurants,
'which is why I thought we should dine early.'

Had he decided this was one way of passing a boring
evening? Glancing at him quickly, Gail thrust the
thought from her mind. If their marriage was proving
unsatisfactory in certain areas, they could always find
plenty to talk about.

Over their meal she asked tentatively what he had
been doing all day. As he didn't seem curious regarding
her own activities, she didn't mention them. As far as
Carl was concerned, her life was an open book. It should
be nice, shouldn't it, to feel mysterious for a change?

She had expected him to answer evasively, for unlike
herself, he could be extremely reticent, so she was
startled when he replied coolly, 'Changing my will, for
one thing.'

Gail wasn't sure why she frowned. It might have been
that his voice was grim again, or simply that for her, as
for many people, any mention of a will brought a cold
feeling.

'Changing your will?' she said slowly. Surely at his
age . . .? She gazed at him, her eyes wide with puzzled
bewilderment. 'Does that mean you'd already made
one?'

'In favour of Petula.' His smile was chilling and she
could see by his eyes that he was hurt and wanted to
hurt her. 'If I'd broken my neck instead of my leg, she
would have done very well.'

Gail heard her spoon fall to her plate with a little
clatter. Her fingers felt numb, so did her voice as she
whispered, 'She married someone else.'

'Which proves she isn't mercenary.'

How had he worked that out? Hysterical laughter welled in Gail's throat. She was relieved as the brief numbness she had experienced spread rapidly through her body, controlling it, enabling her to remark with relative calm, 'So now you've cut her out?'

'It seems a step in the right direction.'

Which, translated, must mean he hadn't yet succeeded? Anger swept through Gail like a tidal wave. 'She would have sold Deanly, you know that, yet you left it to her!'

'Oh, come on, Gail!' Carl laughed, but she could sense he was as angry as she was. 'Women rarely think well of each other, but if she had ever been in a position to, Petula would never have sold Deanly.'

'You're a fool if you believe it.'

Calling him a fool, of course, just had to be a mistake! She saw his face close up, shutting her out, though the hate in his eyes continued speaking to her throughout dinner.

Gail was sure the concert he took her to saved her sanity. At least here, while they sat in stony silence, they could pretend that the music absorbed all their attention. During the interval Carl fetched her light refreshments, then disappeared for a drink, but didn't return until almost the end of the performance. He made no apology for his absence and she didn't look for one. She felt so upset she rather wished he had stayed away.

They were leaving when someone bearing a remarkable resemblance to him approached, forcing him to halt.

'Carl!' the man cried, clearly delighted to see him. 'I've been meaning to look you up, but I've been abroad—just got back, as a matter of fact. I heard you were married?'

He gazed at Gail with a slightly puzzled expression and Carl said sarcastically, 'You heard right for once Jeff. This is my wife,' he introduced them with obvious reluctance. 'Gail, this is a distant cousin of mine, Jeff Lessing.'

So this explained the amazing likeness. Jeff was
younger than Carl and not quite so dark and sombre,
but they might have been brothers rather than cousins.
As Jeff took the hand she held out, she became aware
of his surprise.

'But I thought ...' he began, then broke off in
confusion.

'Petula married someone else,' Carl injected coolly,
his face like a mask compared with his cousin's
embarrassed one.

'I'm out of touch,' Jeff stammered uncomfortably.
Carl's admission had clearly startled him and it was
equally clear that he didn't know what to make of it.
'You haven't been married long, then?' he queried.

'No,' Carl replied briefly, his eyes pointedly on Gail's
hand which Jeff was still holding.

Jeff dropped it quickly but kept on staring, as if
Gail's fair young beauty intrigued him. 'I think you
must be a country girl,' he said. 'There's a refreshing air
about you which isn't usually found in cities.'

'I am.' Gail found it easy to smile at him. He was
nice, she liked him immediately.

Carl cut in brusquely, 'We have to be going.'

Jeff looked disappointed, but rallied. 'I might come
down some time. Would it be all right?'

'No,' Carl snapped, 'it wouldn't!'

'Well, thanks a lot!' Jeff grimaced.

'We haven't a housekeeper,' Carl explained impatiently.

Jeff laughed. 'I can cook and make beds.'

'From what I've heard,' Carl retorted dryly, 'you're
better in them.'

'You weren't very nice to him,' Gail protested, as he
hailed a taxi to take them back to the hotel.

Carl merely shrugged.

'Won't he mind?'

'I shouldn't think so.'

'Does he live in London?' she persisted. She wasn't
really curious, she was using Jeff as a means of bridging

the awful chasm of silence that had lain between Carl and herself during the last hours.

His jaw tightened. 'Jeff lives in London. He was born here, thirty years ago. He's my second cousin and a foreign correspondent. His parents are dead, like yours, like mine, and he's always had an eye for beautiful girls. If, for some reason, he appears to be interested in you, I shouldn't take him too seriously.'

Gail made no attempt to interrupt his monologue, which seemed to spring more from a sudden weariness of spirit than anger. Jeff had reminded him of Petula and, as usual, her heart ached for him. Yet to sympathise with Carl was courting disaster, so she hid her feelings.

At the hotel, a lift took them straight to their rooms. She must have looked a bit depressed, for, after helping her off with her cloak, Carl glanced at her, frowning.

'I seem to have the knack of upsetting you, Gail, and a certain determination, though I don't know why, to keep on doing it. God knows you don't deserve it.'

'Don't worry.' It was her stock reply, and, because he still looked worried, she added for good measure, 'Being married takes getting used to.'

She wasn't surprised when he nodded soberly, but she was when he dropped a cool kiss on her cheek. 'That's for being so understanding.'

Her mouth had never been so envious, but as this was the first time Carl had ever kissed her involuntarily, her eyes glowed.

He stepped back warily and her face flushed as she saw he regretted kissing her. Did he imagine she was about to throw herself at him? Angrily her eyes darkened, she had more pride!

Hastily she moved away from him. She wanted to go to bed but feared, if she did, he might only sit and brood.

'The concert was nice,' she smiled. 'I enjoyed it.'

'Good,' he said crisply, without revealing whether he had or not.

She glanced up at him uncertainly from under her lashes, but he was moving towards the small bar in the corner. Pouring himself a Scotch, he asked what she would like.

'If life's not everything we could wish it to be, this is one way of cheering ourselves up,' he told her.

'No, thanks,' she refused, feeling that even one drink might choke her. She had failed, despite all her attempts, to get closer to him, and though she doubted that he meant her to take his remark seriously, no matter how miserable she was, she knew she would never turn to drink as a means of forgetting how little she meant to him.

CHAPTER FOUR

GAIL said goodnight quickly and retreated to her room. Carl's moods suddenly didn't matter. For once she felt more concerned for her own unhappiness. Getting married had achieved nothing for either of them. The only difference marriage had made was that they could now be miserable together. And even the togetherness was just an illusion; she knew they had never been farther apart.

She took her time getting ready for bed, the dark cloud of misery enveloping her making her movements apathetic. After taking a shower, she put on her dressing-gown until she could find the pyjamas she had stuffed in the bottom of her small suitcase, but before she could find them there was a knock on the door. It could only be Carl. Surprised, Gail raised her head as, after a slight pause, he opened the door and came in.

He had on his bathrobe, the cord carelessly tied round his middle. 'My leg's going mad,' he explained his presence with grim impatience. 'Would it be too much trouble to massage it? I realise you're tired.'

'No, of course not!' As always, when he was in pain, she was eager to relieve it. 'Your bed or mine?'

'Ah!' One brow quirked and she flushed wildly, belatedly conscious of how that must sound, but he merely looked faintly amused. 'The chair will do.'

It was large and comfortable, and as she massaged and kneaded, he settled back with a sigh of relief. Because she kept all her attention fixed on his leg Gail was soon aware that he had nothing on under the robe he was wearing. Strangely it bothered her while it didn't seem to bother him. She felt her pelvic bones tighten, as though fighting against some kind of invasion, and her hands began trembling.

59

'Something wrong?' Carl asked abruptly when she raised her head to stare at him dazedly.

Her heartbeats, more rapid than was warranted by what she was doing, quickened immediately. As their eyes met, the contact was so startling that Gail's eyes widened apprehensively. His nearness was apparently affecting the efficient working of her brain. She was unable to produce even a simple reply. For long moments they stared at each other, like two wild creatures suddenly meeting at night in a forest glade, and not knowing whether to retreat or defend their territory.

His gaze clung to her; in the depth of his eyes a kind of smouldering, sensual awareness was growing to a flame. She had forgotten the thinness of her old wrap which barely concealed the tenderly thrusting curves of her slender figure. She felt suddenly weak and unsteady. Drawing a sharp breath, she incidentally inhaled the male scent of him, the musky smell of his flesh. She had the strange sensation that she was slowly dissolving and flowing into him.

The luminous glow on her face, as these new emotions surged through her, must have given it an inviting expression. Carl began to speak again, then suddenly appeared to change his mind. Her gaze dropped to his mouth and she knew an urgent longing to feel its hardness on hers, to have him kiss her as he had only done once before, on their wedding day.

She saw his hands clench and he stirred, so that the wiry hair of his thighs brushed the smoothness of her palms. With a small gasp, Gail's eyes flew back to his, and this time the silence became interminable and breathless. They seemed to be enclosed in a cocoon of mutual awareness that neither of them could escape.

A powerful attraction was pulling her towards him, yet she was unable to move. When his arms came out to draw her roughly up and into them, her lungs were so constricted she found it difficult to breathe. Carl's strong features were compressed, but he didn't seem to have the willpower to break the trance they were in.

He turned slightly, turning her with him, his hand behind her head, holding it ruthlessly as his mouth descended on hers simultaneously. When his lips moved on hers they were still as hard and cool as when he had kissed her before, but no longer indifferent. They became fierce and increasingly demanding, forcing her lips apart, sensuously exploring. She could feel the heat of his limbs matching the warmth of the blood her pounding heart pumped through her veins, and gave a little moan of surrender. A throbbing desire for him, which until now had lain almost dormant, flamed through her body at his touch, making her yearn to be even closer, She could feel her flesh melting against his while her hungry body longed to be one with him.

Curling against him, she let her response plead for her. Something flowered in her heart, like a wild rose throwing open its petals to the sun. Carl wasn't immune; she sensed the desire in him, almost palpable in its intensity, and feelings such as she had never experienced before in her life were coursing through her in throbbing, indescribable waves. She had both arms round his neck when he jerked his lips from hers and stared at her as if doubting his own sanity.

His arms slackened, though she guessed unconsciously. His chest still rose and fell heavily, his heartbeats hammering into her breast. There was such an obvious struggle going on inside him, she dared not move or speak. He had felt something moving and flowing between them, but he was fighting it. Just as she was praying he would give in, his face hardened and he thrust her off his knee.

'I must have had too much whisky,' he said harshly.

He seemed to be talking to himself. Gail tottered to the bed, not caring if he regarded this as a blatant invitation. She felt wounded, as if part of herself had just been ripped away. It couldn't feel worse, she was sure, to be torn limb from limb.

She looked up sharply and felt the hot colour flood her cheeks as she tried to collect herself. Meeting his eyes, she saw the indecision in his, then the contempt. She felt she had been briefly connected with a new life force on some star-strewn planet, then abruptly thrown back to earth and harsh reality again.

Carl, already on his feet, moved towards the door. 'I'm sorry I kissed you,' he muttered stiffly. 'The next time my leg aches, I'll ignore it.'

Gail lay awake most of the night, trying to come to terms with this unexpected turn of events which promised to turn her life upside down. She had loved Carl when she had married him, but love for her had always been a warm gentle feeling, a desire to care for and even protect him. Those feelings might remain, but a new concept had been added that evening. When she thought of Carl now, his voice, his touch, her heart pounded and her body throbbed with surging waves of heat. She felt shaken and incapable of dealing with such an overwhelming experience.

Tossing and turning, she gazed blindly at the ceiling, trying to think calmly. Her mouth was sore and swollen and she could still feel the pressure of his fingers on the back of her head. These things distracted her as she attempted to organise her thoughts.

Carl had held her, kissed her, but not because she looked more attractive. He was quite oblivious to her improved looks. Something had happened between them, but for him it hadn't been important. He would decide it was a trick of fate, a betrayal of the senses, brought about by the lateness of the hour and perhaps too much to drink. And, not least, because she had been willing and available. He had kissed her before, and on that first morning, before the vet had interrupted them, he had even suggested she went upstairs with him, but he would never, in normal circumstances, come near her. It was Petula whom he still loved.

Gail trembled as she realised that unless she managed to make him forget Petula, their marriage might fail. Evidence of this was growing every day. Carl wasn't indifferent to her. All her senses told her this, despite his frequent and contemptuously expressed remarks which gave the opposite expression. If she were to literally throw herself at him, she had few doubts as to what might take place, but her pride rebelled and she found it difficult to even contemplate doing such a thing. And if she did entice Carl to make love to her, it might only hasten her own downfall, rather than the reverse. As she was completely inexperienced, she might impress him less with her body than she had done with her new face. And she shuddered to imagine what the consequences might be.

The following morning, as they weren't leaving until after lunch, Gail went shopping again. Hoping she hadn't taken leave of her senses, after buying presents for Ruth and Donald, she searched diligently for one special commodity for herself, not giving up until she had found exactly what she wanted. Her purchases were then hidden in the bottom of her bags, not for Carl's eyes until later—if ever! He was occupied all morning with business, but he seemed restored to a relatively pleasant humour as they motored back to Deanly.

No sooner had they arrived than Frank was there with problems. Bob, the jockey who was booked most frequently to ride for them, had gone down with an extremely bad dose of 'flu. He was supposed to be riding for them at the end of the week and might recover in time, but as the race meeting was so close, they dared not risk waiting to see. Then Barley, one of the horses entered for the really big stakes, hadn't been clearing up his feed, which, though not necessarily a bad sign, was one her father hadn't liked to see.

Gail glanced apologetically from Frank's anxious face to Carl's. 'I'd better go.'

He merely shrugged, but as he turned away she noticed he frowned. Instinctively she knew there was something irritating him, but she couldn't think what it could be. As an owner, he left the responsibility for preparing his horses for racing to his trainer. Was it because he didn't believe she was competent enough for

the job that he was frowning, even though he refused
to replace her or let Frank take over?

He slipped into another of his black moods during
the next few days, and Gail rarely saw him apart from
meals. Even these he sometimes skipped and if he slept
at all it was in his study. With a sigh which was half
regret, half relief, she put away the seductive
nightgowns she had bought in London, telling herself
she had been crazy ever to think of them in the first
place.

In the middle of the week, to the surprise of them
both, Jeff Lessing walked in.

'Blame your wife,' he grinned, at Carl's not very
welcoming expression. 'I heard that she trains your
horses and isn't just a pretty face, so being a reporter, I
had to come and see for myself.'

'And your reputation as a wife-chaser,' Carl
responded dryly, 'what about that? Just remember mine
is out of bounds.'

'I'll remember,' Jeff promised, the laughter in his eyes
proving he wasn't mortally offended, encouraging Gail
to explain how she was only helping out until Carl
found someone else.

'I waited several months for your father,' Carl said
shortly. 'Finding a satisfactory trainer isn't easily
accomplished overnight. But I've heard of a good man
who might be interested in moving in as soon as
possible.'

While Jeff nodded and Carl changed the conversation
on to another topic, Gail tried not to glare at him in
hurt surprise. Wouldn't you think he would have
mentioned it before now, she thought, instead of telling
her about it in front of another person! She couldn't
pretend she wouldn't be relieved to be relieved of a job
which was becoming almost too much for her, but she
wished Carl had chosen to tell her she was about to
become redundant in a different way.

For all she had pestered him for weeks about a
trainer, now that the moment of his arrival was almost

upon them she felt curiously resentful, and not merely because of how Carl had gone about it. Suspecting she had been unconsciously hoping that he would consider her own expertise adequate, she frowned impatiently at the contrariness of human nature. All the time she had pestered him, had she been secretly hoping for quite a different decision from the one he had obviously reached? Surely, though, he could have told her he was definitely on the lookout for a new trainer, instead of leaving her in the dark.

She left them talking and went to make some tea. To her surprise Carl followed her to the kitchen. He sat on the edge of the table, one long leg dangling, the other on the floor, watching her consideringly.

'Are you offended about the trainer?' he asked at last.

Gail bent over the teapot to hide her face. She had felt his glance going coolly over her and guessed what was coming and didn't want him to see how foolishly disappointed she was.

'No,' she managed to sound quite convincing. 'We've needed someone long enough—I just thought you might have told me.'

He didn't apologise. 'Sometimes, Gail, it's not easy to see the future clearly. You come to a crossroads and it's shrouded in mist and you're not sure which way to go. If you aren't careful you can take the wrong turning, and it's not always easy to reverse. This may sound dramatic but, believe me, I've been doing a lot of thinking lately. I've found a trainer who's ready for retirement in a couple of years' time and is quite willing to help me run the training side down. I find I'd rather concentrate on breeding and a slightly quieter life. So perhaps now you can understand why I didn't talk about it, how such a decision had to be mine alone.'

It was too much to assimilate all at once. There was a dazed expression in the eyes Gail turned to look at him. Was it possible she had misjudged the situation?

'I had no idea you were thinking of giving up

training,' she said. 'I thought you'd lost interest because of Petula.'

His eyes hardened, any warmth immediately leaving them. 'Can't you leave Petula out of anything? My feelings for her have nothing to do with the stables.'

He certainly knew how to hurt! And how could he so coolly deny he had been a changed man since Petula had left him? Forcing words of accusation back down her throat, Gail said bleakly, 'After racing for so long, won't you miss it?'

'Not really,' he retorted curtly. 'My father was the enthusiast, not me. After he died I just carried on, maybe as you're doing, without really stopping to think. After I close the yard, if I have a promising yearling, I might have him trained, but it won't be here.'

So it was the end of the road—and maybe for her as well. Gail's face went pale. She knew little about breeding, certainly she could learn, but it wouldn't be necessary. Carl would no longer need her. 'What will I do?' she whispered, more to herself.

'You'll still be an owner's wife, won't you?' Carl eased his long length impatiently from the table. 'You'll still be able to find plenty to do, if you're willing.'

Unhappily she said, 'Somehow I can't see myself on the racecourse, dressed up to the nines in a big, floppy hat, dispensing regal smiles on your occasional winner. It won't be like taking an actual part in it. Maybe I could start my own training establishment?'

'Some women do, but I don't believe it's for you.' He stepped nearer, his voice softer. 'Gail, I know how you feel, I'd be pretty insensitive if I didn't, but once you've recovered from the initial shock, I'm sure you'll begin to see things my way. When this new man arrives you can have a rest. You've never stopped lately and it's beginning to show.'

'Thanks!' If she sounded childishly petulant, Gail suddenly didn't care! Better that than bursting into tears. Not only was Carl hinting that her looks were deteriorating instead of improving, but he seemed to be telling her, as clearly as if he had put it in words, that he was still in love with Petula! As for his being tired of the yard, she didn't know what to make of it. Wasn't it more likely that he planned to get rid of it so that if Petula ever returned, he would have no real ties and would be able to take her away?

Picking up the tea-tray with a flounce, she disregarded his angry expression. 'Jeff will be wondering where we've got to,' she said stiffly, sticking her chin in the air and vowing, no matter what happened, she would try and keep it there.

Jeff installed himself in what he called his usual room, which proved he wasn't a stranger to Deanly. Gail didn't remember him, but as she had never mixed much with Carl's guests, that wasn't surprising. Over dinner, which he helped to cook, he kept repeating that he couldn't understand how he had missed her, and, after the setback she believed she had received from Carl regarding her looks, she found this comforting.

That evening, trying to keep all her worries regarding the future at bay until she had time to get them properly sorted out, she had concentrated on her appearance. In a long silky skirt and skimpy top, she was sure she looked very attractive. If she had had any doubts, Jeff's admiring glances would soon have dispelled them. Carl, on the other hand, barely glanced at her, though, during the meal, he did sit very close to her. She knew better than to put this down as a sign of jealousy, however. It was more likely to be sheer possessiveness. He always disliked sharing anything he considered belonged to him.

Jeff was so like Carl in looks that when he laughed and teased her she was tempted to forget he wasn't.

'The resemblance is remarkable,' she said thoughtfully, when Jeff disappeared for a few minutes after dinner to make a phone call, leaving her alone with Carl.

His frown was thoughtful. 'Other people have noticed, but you're the first to suggest it's that close.'

'Anyway, he's very nice.' It seemed easier to talk of Jeff than the subject which must be at the back of both their minds.

'Again like me, would you say?'

Carl's mouth curled, she was sure not with amusement. There seemed only one reply she could make, 'You can be nice when you want to be.'

'Which you've told me before,' he drawled dryly. 'My fault, I suppose, for fishing.'

Lines of puzzlement appeared between Gail's feathery brows. 'Would you rather I told you you were horrible?'

He laughed ruefully at such frankness. 'My father used to say that the truth was preferable to anything else, but now I'm not so sure!'

Gail gazed at him, feeling the usual tug of her senses. He had leaned forward to speak to her and she was intensely conscious of him beside her. The sense of intimacy, for all it wasn't real, filled her with an amazing pleasure. As their eyes met, she would have given anything to have been able to throw herself in his arms, to experience again the excitement and passion of his kisses.

She felt mortified as Carl read the invitation on her face and withdrew. Incoherently, scarcely realising what she was saying, she muttered, 'Jeff will be good company when you're out and I'm not so busy.'

'The new trainer isn't here yet,' Carl snapped. 'And you'd be wise to remember Jeff's been around.'

'You make him sound like a menace.'

'He could be—and he fancies you.'

She swallowed, utterly surprised. Until now she was sure Carl had never considered another man could find her attractive. Half-formed thoughts drifted wistfully through her mind. If only she could convince him she was attractive, might he not stop thinking so much of Petula?

'Carl . . .' she began huskily, then suddenly found herself swept into his arms. She was held helpless in his powerful embrace as, before she could protest, his warm lips crushed down on hers. Then, as she was just as swiftly released, she realised why he had kissed her. Jeff was standing looking at them, a hint of envy and resignation in his eyes, while Carl's gleamed with derisive amusement.

This time Gail was sure Carl was merely acting like any male animal staking out his territory, but while such a dog-in-the-manger attitude incensed her, something advised her to store it away for future reference. She had no idea why, for the kiss he had bestowed on her had held so little affection she just wanted to forget it. Confused, she found herself blushing like a schoolgirl and was glad to escape when Carl suggested coolly that it would be nice to have some coffee.

The second evening of Jeff's visit, they sat in the study discussing the forthcoming race meeting at Newmarket. Jeff, seeming familiar with every horse that had run there, aroused Gail's curiosity.

'How is it you know so much about racing?' she asked.

He laughed, the usual admiration in his eyes as he glanced at her. 'I was reared on it.'

'Really?'

'Sure,' he grinned, then sobered. 'I was brought up in my uncle's stables. He reared me with his foals, a lone orphan . . .'

'I could weep!' Carl drawled.

Jeff grinned again but ignored him. 'I had four cousins, my uncle's sons, all robust fighting men. They got on well, with my uncle standing between them so they couldn't see to shoot each other, and when he died and wasn't there any more to prevent such a calamity happening, they decided to sell up, divide the proceeds and go their separate ways.'

Gail giggled. 'My Irish grandmother would have loved you!' Then she frowned. 'But what happened to you?'

Jeff shrugged carelessly. 'I was at university, at the time, and had always had a fancy for journalism and travel. It seemed sort of natural to graduate from newspaper work to being a foreign correspondent with TV.'

Gail was interested. She said eagerly, 'You must like working abroad or you wouldn't do it, but isn't it often very dangerous? I've seen pictures of newsmen standing in the middle of the fighting. You must be very brave!'

'He is,' Carl cut in grimly, 'all foreign correspondents are, but if you don't shut up you'll have him creeping under the table.'

'I was only . . .' she began, when he interrupted again, 'I'm sure he doesn't want to talk about his gory adventures. He usually comes here to forget them.'

'Oh, I'm sorry,' Gail stammered, feeling ready to sink through the floor.

Jeff smiled at her, his eyes gentle. 'Carl's only teasing, but a lot of people might be right to be sceptical. I'm not sure whether it's braveness or numbness that sees a man through these situations. I know I frequently feel scared to death—and it's often all around me when bombs and bullets are flying. I think you forget your own fears, though, when you realise they're nothing compared to the plight others are in. What makes me forget myself completely and go really berserk are the maimed and starving women and children. It makes me ashamed to be a man.'

'Some things must be worth fighting for?' Gail frowned, wondering if anything could justify such terrible devastation as Jeff described.

'Personal freedom,' Jeff shrugged grimly. 'But even that can be a misconception. People strive for independence and when they get it they don't know how to handle it. Frequently they're merely exchanging the régime they complain about for a much worse one, which can't be so easily got rid of. The world clamours, give them their freedom, then ignores the death and destruction it can bring. I believe the price is often far too high.'

While she nodded, this time it was Carl who answered him verbally, and for the next hour she listened as the two men discussed the mounting troubles which beset mankind. Occasionally she joined in, but for the most part she was content to listen and learn. Carl had travelled widely and was as well informed as Jeff, but she prayed he would never be exposed to such dangers. As she watched him talking all this was revealed in her beautiful green eyes, she didn't notice Jeff glancing at her thoughtfully.

The next few days before Newmarket were busy and, for Gail, nostalgic. She met the new trainer; Carl did, in fact invite him to lunch and for a look over the establishment. He was moving in at the beginning of the following week. Dick Noble was a pleasant man in his early sixties and Gail was sure they would get on, but when he arrived she knew her responsibilities would be over. Thereafter, she would be welcome on the gallops and to potter round the stables, but no one would rely on her any more.

'Never take a sip of power,' her father used to say, 'unless you're sure of being able to take a good long drink. It's addictive.' Now Gail was coming to realise the truth of his words, and it didn't make her any happier. Yet, at the same time, she had to admit she had no desire to become a full-time trainer. Hinting to Carl that she might was one thing, putting it into practice quite another.

If Carl had loved her, she would have been quite content to be his wife. It was because he didn't love her and she feared he would soon tire of her and ask her to leave that she felt forced to face the future squarely and try and decide what she must do. Probably the best thing would be to find a job in some other stables and see how she got on.

It might have been easier had she been able to talk to someone about all her doubts and fears. She was tempted to confide in Ruth and Donald, or even Jeff, but as her problems concerning her marriage involved Carl as well as herself, that wasn't possible. She could only continue to hope that Carl would eventually fall in love with her.

They had two horses running at Newmarket, and these were dispatched in the modern horsebox which they used every time. Frank went with them, along with the travelling head lad and their excellent driver. Among them, they would ensure that the animals reached the course safe and sound. A good driver was essential as bad cornering and hard braking could make a horse almost impossible to load when he went out again.

At the course the head lad would see to most things, but for the others, there would still be plenty to do. Frank had to check that the horses were properly entered and must make sure the jockey had arrived and weighed in, and, later that he was wearing the right colours. Then the horse which was running had to be saddled up before being taken into the paddock. Normally all plans as to how a horse was to be ridden, or handled, would be discussed long before this, but sometimes, as Gail well knew there might be last-minute adjustments, and it wasn't until after the race that such changes might be proved wise or foolish!

Newmarket had been the headquarters of racing since the seventeenth century, and, as at Lambourn, strings of horses were to be seen on the roads and heath. The heath itself was dotted with the cupolas and turrets of racing stables. The National Stud was next to the racecourse, just south-west of the town, and the home of the Jockey Club, the controlling body of British racing, was in the High Street. Gail had been here many times with her father and Carl and occasionally they had allowed her to attend the bloodstock sales with them, which were held during the spring and autumn at Park Paddocks.

The open heath was popular with royalty in 1605, for

hunting and hawking, and records of horse-racing went back as far as 1622. In 1664, the Newmarket Town Plate was first run, possibly the oldest established race still going. Charles II decreed that it should be run on the second Thursday in October for ever, and, apart from wartime, his command has been obeyed. It was for amateur riders and there was no money to be won, just sausages and riding equipment, but it was very good fun.

Gail drove to Newmarket with Jeff and Carl. Sometimes, if they were going greater distances, they shared a helicopter or small plane with other stables. It made a great difference, especially if there was evening racing. Today, however, they travelled in Carl's car.

After lunch, Carl made Gail stay with Jeff while he went to check with Frank that everything was all right. Carl had been to several race meetings lately, which she had taken for a good sign, but now that he had told her he was giving up, she didn't know what to make of it. Was Petula behind such a decision, she wondered, or was he telling the truth when he declared he had never been all that interested in the training side of things? Gail sighed unhappily. She had married Carl believing she had two battles on her hands, one against his increasing apathy, the other against Petula. Yet now that she was left with only Petula to contend with her prospects of success seemed bleaker than ever. Carl didn't look any happier for having made a decision about the stables. If anything he was a great deal grimmer.

'The usual crowd,' Jeff murmured in her ear.

She turned her head to smile at him. She had been paying attention to the crowd herself, while lost in thought. Nowadays she was always on the lookout for Petula, with no clear idea as to what she would do if she saw her.

'Yes,' she replied absently. There was no sign of Petula and she recognised three American owners who had horses running that afternoon. Swiftly she ran her eyes over the veritable sea of faces, her brain ticking off names like a computer, forgetting Jeff was watching her closely.

'Looking for somebody special?'

She started, flushing a little. 'Not really.'

'Ah,' he studied her guilty face thoughtfully, 'me thinks the lady twists the truth slightly? A certain Mrs Lee Oscar comes to mind.'

Hanging her head, Gail bit her lip sharply. 'Am I that transparent?'

Quickly he laid a concerned hand on her arm. 'Just to me. No one would guess. I have this built-in instinct about people which often tells me more than I want to know.'

Gail swallowed, without looking up. 'He still loves her.'

'Thinks he does, you mean.'

Bitter laughter escaped her lips. 'If there's a difference he hasn't noticed.'

Jeff frowned, hesitating. 'Did you know this when you married him?'

Gail nodded miserably.

'Then why . . .?'

Hearing the controlled amazement in his voice, she raised her head, trying to speak carelessly. 'Plenty of reasons. The main one being, I suppose, that we were useful to each other.'

'Hmm,' said Jeff slowly. 'You're probably going to tell me it's none of my business, but between meeting you in London and coming to Deanly, I learnt a few things. I gather our Petula deserted Carl in his hour of need and he more or less went to pieces?'

'I didn't realise it was such common knowledge!' Gail said sharply.

'And you've lived in the racing world all your life!' he retorted dryly.

Her dark eyes appealed for his forgiveness. 'I'm sorry, Jeff. You're right, of course, and I shouldn't have snapped. But it made me so mad! It still makes me mad.

He only broke his leg, for heaven's sake! It wasn't as though he was marred for life. Just a broken leg and a spell of bad luck.'

Jeff nodded. 'It would be enough. Petula always hated anything that wasn't perfect, be it a man's health or his luck. She must have been horrified out of her mean little mind. It wouldn't make any difference who it was. She took fright, and another man happened to be there at the time. I'd say that was Oscar's misfortune and that Carl is well rid of her.'

Gail sighed. It should have cheered her immensely that Jeff understood Petula completely, but how could it alter anything unless Carl did? She said as much to Jeff.

He frowned consideringly. 'He must be blind if he can't see how desirable you are,' he said finally. 'But I can see you have a problem. Petula did exercise a powerful influence and I imagine it would take something equally powerful to break it.'

'You can say that again!' Gail muttered under her breath as Carl returned. She might be Carl's wife, but any influence she had would never be strong enough to even dent the feelings he had for Petula!

Before the first race, she was startled by the number of people who came up to congratulate Carl on his marriage and wish them well. It was the first time they had been at a race meeting together since their wedding, and Gail was touched by the obvious sincerity of the good wishes showered on them. Her father had been a much respected, even famous trainer, and Gail a familiar figure as his daughter, but she was surprised to discover the amount of notice that had been taken of her.

'I didn't realise you were so popular,' Carl teased, as he steered her towards the owners' stand with Jeff behind them. 'I feel as though I'm married to a public figure!'

'Clothes make a difference,' she said lightly. 'People aren't used to seeing me dressed up.'

His dark brows quirked as he slanted a long glance at

her and there was surprise in his voice. 'You're looking amazingly attractive. I like your outfit.'

Surely he had noticed before now? She had been wearing it all morning! 'It cost plenty,' she said.

Then suddenly she realised he was no longer with her. His eyes, as hers had been doing an hour ago, were searching the enclosures. It came like an excruciating blow to realise that they were both searching for the same woman, one that one of them hated but the other loved!

CHAPTER FIVE

DESPITE such terrifying evidence that Petula was still very much on his mind, Gail felt a small thrill of pride as she sat beside Carl for the first time as his wife. On the racecourse her father had always looked after her. Carl might have been there, but usually in the company of some glamorous girl-friend. If he had spared Gail a glance it had been to see if she was behaving herself. Now, as he concluded his visual exploration of the other stands and gave her his attention again, she was reassured by another glint of what she took to be appreciation in his eyes. It made all the bother of dressing up seem much more worthwhile.

One of their horses came in second, after almost beating the Irish colt that won, but when their other horse passed the post first in the next race. Gail was on her feet, dancing up and down with excitement.

She always got a little carried away, even when their horses didn't win, but today she was jubilant. Her voice was hoarse from shouting encouragement as Midget moved out in front, their jockey, with luck and good judgment, managing to do everything right. When Bob in a splendid ride, brought Midget in to win by three clear lengths, Gail hadn't any breath left.

Unable to speak, there was only one way she could express her feelings. Throwing her race card in the air, her face radiantly alight, she flung her arms round Carl's neck, hugging and kissing him ecstatically. She was so ablaze with triumph and relief, she couldn't contain herself. He grinned amidst the general uproar and kissed her back, seeming to catch some of her uninhibited excitement. For a few moments, his hard sombre face softened to something very near tenderness.

77

He kept hold of her arm while she laughingly turned to Jeff, kissing him as well.

'Hi!' he protested mockingly, as she kissed Jeff twice, 'that's more than enough for him!'

In excellent spirits they hurried down to the track so that Carl could lead the winner in. Gail stayed close by him, not trying to hide how delighted she was over the way things had gone. Everyone at Deanly knew she had been responsible for training the two horses to the high standard they had reached today. Although she had had help and advice, the final decisions regarding their feeding and training programmes had been hers alone. If she had no official status, no one was taking any notice of that. She had won a big race and there was no shortage of congratulations.

It was a day she would always remember—the crowds, the sunshine, the triumph, all shared with Carl. As Jeff found her hat, sliding it back on her gleaming head before their photographs were taken, she wasn't ashamed of the tears in her eyes. It was a good feeling, going out in a blaze of glory. It almost made up for the sadness she felt that it could never happen again.

They managed to leave reasonably early, although it was difficult to get away. They were stopped by so many people wanting to talk to them, and showered with invitations. Sir Arthur, Carl's uncle, an inveterate racegoer, embraced Gail warmly and asked them both to lunch the following day. He extended the invitation to Jeff, who he declared, beaming, was one of his favourite relations.

At Deanly, when the rest of the outfit returned there was to be a small party. They didn't celebrate every time they won a race, not even the very big ones. This spring, so far, there had been no parties at all. When Carl insisted they gave one this evening, he had smiled and said it was in her honour, and she wondered happily if he was trying to make up for his ill humour of the past.

They had barely got in when the telephone rang. It

was for Jeff, from London. His boss had been trying to get in touch with him all afternoon. A new assignment had come up and he wanted Jeff there immediately.

'I have to be in the office first thing in the morning,' Jeff explained with a wry smile, 'and by first thing, Harry always means six o'clock. He'll expect me to be packed by then too, ready to leave at a moment's notice for heaven knows where?'

'But I thought you'd just got back from somewhere?' Gail said quickly.

'Yes, well——' Jeff grimaced lightly, 'that's life, isn't it? I was warned this might happen, so I can't complain.'

Couldn't he? Gail wasn't so sure. He still looked tired, surely he deserved a few more days?

Carl glanced at him with a frown, aware of the strain on his cousin's face, despite the indifference he pretended. 'Do you intend going back to London tonight, Jeff?' he asked.

Jeff nodded. 'Yes, right away. It's perhaps a good job they rang before we started to celebrate.'

Ten minutes later he was saying goodbye. He shook hands with Carl, but his eyes were on Gail. Taking her in his arms, ignoring Carl, he kissed her full on the lips. 'Think of me,' he whispered huskily. 'I'll be back.'

Neither Gail nor Carl spoke as he leapt into his brilliant red sports car and roared off down the drive.

Watching him disappear, Carl said severely, 'I should think he has enough troubles without you adding to them.'

Gail's startled gaze left the drive to swing to him. 'How would you say I've done that?'

'By encouraging him, allowing him to kiss you and kissing him back.'

She frowned. What sort of game was Carl playing? 'Surely kissing a man goodbye couldn't be said to be encouraging him?'

'It was the way you responded,' Carl retorted coldly, 'putting your arms round his neck. Jeff's very vulnerable.'

She had placed her hands on Jeff's shoulders to try and push him away, an involuntary reaction she saw no reason to discuss with Carl. 'Only a few days ago,' she replied sharply, 'you were warning me against him! I can't believe that big bad wolves change overnight.'

Carl stared at her grimly for long seconds, seemingly lost in thought. 'You're right, of course. So why am I making all this fuss? One would think I was jealous!'

Which was impossible, he was implying, obviously talking to himself. Gail sighed, turning her wistful eyes to the drive and fields again. If only Carl was jealous, instead of merely examining his own feelings without attaching any real importance to them. He was studying them like he might a field of weeds, wondering where to start and pull out!

'I haven't fallen for Jeff, or encouraged him,' she said slowly, 'nor do I believe he's fallen for me. I'm going to miss him, though,' she added. 'He's very like you.'

'How? I fail to see any resemblance, unless you mean physically.'

'That must be it,' she agreed lightly, realising she couldn't be more explicit. Jeff, to her, was a younger, happier version of Carl, without his serious involvement with another woman. He liked her, perhaps more than Carl did, but his kiss hadn't disturbed her like a bolt of lightning, as Carl's did. She had felt nothing but the hard warmth of his mouth, there hadn't been anything else. The allegiance of her mind and body to Carl was unbreakable, but she could imagine his embarrassment if she told him so.

'Jeff appeals to you,' Carl snapped, when she didn't elaborate, 'because he's like what you'd like me to be.'

'I don't know,' she tried to answer his startling astuteness truthfully. 'I couldn't be sure.' She looked down the empty drive. 'I hope he'll be all right. You know, the other night, when he began talking, I got the impression that he feels things more deeply than he lets on.'

'Don't you think I do?'

'You?'

'You said I was like him.'

His attitude was suddenly different. He was staring at her and she could scarcely face the intensity in his eyes. It might not be consciously intentional but, amazingly, he appeared to be shutting Jeff out, concentrating suddenly on the two of them. It came to her then that he had a deeper understanding of his cousin than she had at first thought. She could tell him nothing about Jeff that he didn't already know or suspect, but he was discovering an interest in herself which was beginning to intrigue him, even against his will.

She might never hold him enthralled, as Petula did, but he had been slightly annoyed when Jeff had kissed her and she could never recall him being even remotely bothered over anything like that before. Jeff finding her attractive must have given him food for thought, yet there was something more than mere curiosity regarding another man's interest in the eyes that were suddenly closely and darkly scanning her smooth young features.

Shaking herself out of the trance which appeared to be threatening them both, Gail said hastily, 'I promised Frank I'd do the evening rounds. I shouldn't like him to come back and find they're still to do.'

In most yards the staff returned at five or six o'clock, to groom and see to their horses. This was a very important period of the working day for the trainer too. It was then that the general fitness and feeding programme of each horse might be discussed and adjustments made. If there was anything wrong the trainer and the head lad would decide whether or not to call the vet. Usually the head lad was half vet himself through years of experience.

Carl said brusquely, 'I'll do the rounds, this evening. You have enough to do here.' When she began protesting, he said curtly, 'I don't want to argue.'

Gail was so surprised she didn't. Carl had scarcely

been near the stables this year and had never offered to take her place before to do the evening stint. As they turned to go inside, she saw it was getting quite late. She supposed she ought to be thinking of the party. The staff wouldn't say anything, but she could imagine their thoughts if there was nothing ready.

While she searched for glasses and plates and paper napkins, Carl went upstairs. He reappeared a few minutes later, dressed in working clothes.

'I'll have to change again when I come back,' he said, 'but it can't be helped. Can you manage until I get back?' he asked, glancing at her keenly.

Warmed that he seemed to care, Gail smiled at him gratefully. He was wearing tan cotton slacks with a checked shirt. The shirt was open at the neck, exposing the strong, tanned lines of it, in a peculiar way making her heart race.

'You look all right as you are. I shouldn't bother to change again.'

'Perhaps not,' he agreed. 'But that wasn't the question. I asked if you could manage.'

'I'd have to be stupid if I couldn't!' she laughed. 'The food you ordered has arrived,' he had ordered it from Newmarket, from a catering firm, and she'd found it in the kitchen. 'All I have to do is set it out.'

'Do some of it,' he said firmly, 'then go and have a shower. You must be feeling in need of one, and I'll finish off when I come back.'

After he had gone, Gail put some beer in the fridge, then did as she was told. But she didn't admit the wisdom of Carl's advice until she was under the shower. Not until the water began draining the weariness from her limbs did she realise how tired she was. It had been a long day, as well as a traumatic one, and the evening was still to come.

The shower did her so much good, she could have stayed under it all night. She did, in fact, linger so long she didn't leave herself much time to dress, and the silky creation she chose at random looked very transparent once she had it on. She would have changed it for something else if she had happened to glance at her full-length reflection before doing her face and hair. Then it seemed too late to begin all over again, especially as Carl might be back and wondering where she had got to.

Gail frowned as she adjusted a shoulder strap and gazed doubtfully at her small, abandoned image. The dress was respectable enough, she couldn't believe anyone would think it wasn't. She was convinced she was merely imagining it looked suggestive.

Impatiently she shook her head, making her fair hair dance in gleaming disorder. She had no desire to turn into a modern siren, but she did wish she had been lovely enough to make Carl fall in love with her. Jeff had said it would take something powerful to break the hold Petula had over him, and no weapons she possessed, in the way of either looks or personality, could ever be described as powerful!

She had thought, when they'd got home, that Carl was beginning to take an interest in her, but remembering the gaunt shadow of strain on his face as he had searched round Newmarket for Petula, Gail told herself bitterly not to be so foolish. As for Jeff's advice, she would be wiser to forget it. If Carl didn't turn to her on his own accord, she wasn't going to throw herself at him.

Despondently she returned to the kitchen, finding Carl's mood better than her own. She had put a thin shawl over her shoulders, so she didn't feel as naked as she had upstairs. He was busy unpacking cartons of food and glanced up with a smile.

The blue of his eyes darkened with appreciation. 'You look charming.'

Beneath the warmth of his smile, her heart accelerated its beat and she immediately felt happier. His remark might have been casual, but it gave her an inordinate sense of pleasure.

'Thanks!' Her eyes glowed at him while her cheeks flushed enchantingly.

As their eyes met, a frown appeared in his and he returned his attention to the table again.

Gail gazed at his bent head. Now what was he thinking? He was so changeable. One moment meeting her more than halfway, the next retreating grimly. A man like Carl would deny ever retreating from anything but she wished she could understand his moods!

He was observing wryly, 'I think they've sent enough food to feed an army.'

'Umm.' Attempting to concentrate on what he was saying, she glanced over the array of savouries and cakes. 'Wilkinsons are good caterers, though.'

'I just hope our guests are hungry enough to demolish this little lot.'

They were talking like strangers, and she was relieved to hear the sound of trucks outside. 'They must have heard, they seem to be arriving,' she commented, forcing a cheerful grin.

Carl's employees were friends as well as staff. The party was soon under way, and everyone seeming to be talking and eating at once. As the beer flowed so did the stories, the reminiscing growing more exaggerated as the evening progressed. The married members of the staff had brought their wives, who joined in the fun wholeheartedly, with amusing anecdotes of their own. They were like a big happy family, Gail mused, gazing round the crowd of animated faces.

Before she made coffee, Carl put his arm round her and proposed a toast, 'To my wife.' As he raised his glass, the others enthusiastically followed suit while Gail, quite overwhelmed, tried to thank them. She wasn't sure if they knew yet of Carl's plans for running down the stables, and it made her heart ache when she thought of the friends she would lose when they finally closed. Not all of them would have to go, but many of them would.

It was well after midnight before the last of them departed, and the door had barely closed behind them when Carl turned on her, asking curtly, 'Do you think that dress was quite suitable?'

She coloured and picked up an empty glass. 'You said I looked charming.'

Removing the glass from her hands, he put it down again. 'You were wearing a shawl.'

She had discarded the shawl when the room had grown hot. 'What is it about my dress that you're objecting to exactly?' she asked defiantly, suspecting she already knew.

'It's too low—isn't *décolleté* the word?—at the front.'

He spoke so disapprovingly she had to hang on to her temper. 'So what?' she said, disdaining to answer. 'Anyway, it was a nice party.'

'Yes!' he snapped.

'Probably not many people recognised me in a dress,' she giggled, 'they're so used to seeing me in pants.'

Deliberately, he might have been punishing her flippancy, Carl let his gaze roam closely over her, lingering thoughtfully on the delicate contours of her breasts.

'Have you got anything on underneath?'

'No, I haven't!' she was flustered at last and hated him that he could so easily bring the colour flooding to her face. 'But—you can't tell, can you?' she stammered.

He laughed cynically, 'It doesn't take X-ray eyes.'

She suddenly realised he was angry, which puzzled her. 'We're living in the 1980's, Carl,' she frowned. 'I know I'm your wife, but is there any need to be so—Victorian?'

'You aren't my wife, though, are you?' he muttered, diverting contemptuously. 'We went through a ceremony, but that's as far as we got.'

'Do I have to tell you why?' she cried, suddenly enraged that he could be so callous.

He went pale. 'Bitch!' he snarled. 'Do you always have to remind me of her?'

Somehow Gail felt she could stand no more. 'I'm going to bed, Carl, I'm tired.'

'So'm I,' he muttered, his anger fading coldly. 'I'll just lock up here.'

She trailed upstairs without mentioning the dirty cups
and glasses. If she started on them, he would order her
to leave them, and she was too weary to argue. She
tried not to wonder how she would get through
everything in the morning. So much to do before they
went to Sir Arthur's for lunch! Suddenly, as she walked
upstairs, all the cares in the world seemed to be
toppling down on top of her.

Carl must have been quick, because he entered their
bedroom directly behind her.

Finding his robe, he turned to leave again. 'I'll have a
shower,' he said abruptly. 'I feel filthy.'

He probably did, as he'd been busy all day. Gail
mumbled something as he went out. He didn't use the
bathroom which was part of this suite; he used the one
across the landing. To begin with, Gail had been
grateful for such an arrangement, now she wasn't so
sure.

Shrugging such controversial thoughts from her, she
swiftly undressed. Even though he granted her the
privacy of her own bathroom, since Jeff's arrival he had
slept in his own bed. Apparently he hadn't wanted Jeff
to guess he wasn't sleeping with his wife. He and his
cousin had usually talked until the early hours and she
had often been asleep when he had come upstairs, but
once she had woken up and seen him lying next to her,
so close she could have put her hand out and touched
him, had she dared.

Now, half-formed pieces of intelligence seemed to be
trying to penetrate her brain. She tried not to take any
notice, but they wouldn't go away. As she returned
from her own ablutions and reached for her pyjamas, it
occurred to her that tonight, because he was tired, Carl
might decide to sleep here again.

Frowning, she paused, feeling more than a little
feverish. Jeff had said it would take something powerful
to break the hold Petula had over him, and the most
powerful weapon she had might be herself. If she gave
herself to Carl, forgetting such things as pride and

common sense, and proved she could be a real and satisfactory wife, might she not soon wield a far greater influence than someone thousands of miles away? If she let Carl make love to her and it saved their marriage, wouldn't it be worthwhile?

If such a question had crossed her mind in the light of day, she knew she would have dismissed it derisively. Being a temptress, no matter how desperate the circumstances, didn't come naturally. But here in the dark, if she crept into Carl's bed and could manage to utter a few encouraging words when he found her—if he found her—it might be much easier. He could always turn and walk away and tomorrow they could pretend it had never happened.

It was now or never, Gail decided, clutching her pyjamas tightly, as if they presented departing sanity. One of these days Petula would return—wasn't fate always playing unkind tricks? And if by then she wasn't firmly established in Carl's life, she wouldn't give much for her chances of survival?

Frightening thoughts of Petula finally propelled Gail towards the drawer where, hidden and so far unworn, her satin nightgowns lay. She remembered with what high hopes she had bought them and how she had eventually come to wish she had never seen them. Blindly she opened the drawer, reaching for the first one she came to. Dragging it out, she pulled it clumsily over her head. With luck it didn't tear, neither then or when she dived into Carl's big double bed. She had to clench her teeth and just about everything else to try and stop shaking. Even so, she trembled like a leaf.

She had put out the light before finding her nightdress, relying on the moon for illumination. She had a wild desire to pile the duvet completely on top of her so she wouldn't see Carl turn away when he noticed her under it. He would most likely imagine she'd had too much to drink and had got into the wrong bed by mistake. Rather than disturb her, he might use hers. She tried to smile, picturing him trying to accommodate himself in its shorter length, but somehow it didn't seem funny.

He wasn't long. Hearing his footsteps approaching, she pretended to be asleep. As he opened the door, he switched off the light in the corridor but didn't bother to put the bedroom one on, which must have made it seem briefly darker than it actually was. Gail held her breath as he walked towards the bed, his footsteps dragging slightly, as if he was weary. A wave of tenderness swept over her and she knew it would be no hardship to be able to comfort him.

Carl's hand groped for the sheet. He raised it and suddenly paused. She heard his breath draw in sharply. 'Gail?'

Something of her unconscious, girlish fears must have shown as she opened her eyes. As they widened, he went entirely still.

'Did you think I'd be returning to the study tonight?'

'I . . .' It was all she could get out before her voice failed her.

'Have you always slept in my bed when I wasn't here?' he frowned. 'I don't recall seeing you in it before.'

Suddenly she had to make him understand, he was already turning away. What would happen to all her plans if she lay here like a cowardly idiot! 'I haven't been here before,' she whispered.

He stiffened, and again her courage wavered when she raised her head to meet his immediately narrowed gaze. 'If this is some kind of joke,' he said between his teeth, 'would you kindly explain?'

'Carl,' ignoring the shame burning her cheeks, she forced herself to go on, 'do I have to? I thought you would understand.'

He was little more than a large shadow against the darkness of the room, but she saw his hands clench. That he didn't leave her immediately seemed to suggest that some part of him, at least, wanted to stay. She could feel the terrible tension inside her bringing tears to her cheeks. Desperately hoping he didn't see them, she stared up at him, her eyes glinting green, like spring corn, her hair waving over the pillows, the pale colour of the ripening wheat.

Their eyes met, striking into each other, as had happened once before, in the London hotel. Carl's mouth tightened and she knew he was employing all his powers to combat whatever impulses her proximity might be rousing in him. His mind was so clearly fighting for supremacy over his body that she feared she had already lost!

So overwrought she dared not stop to analyse her feelings, she grasped his hand, holding it to her cheek, trying to give substance to what she was trying to tell him. Words were now quite beyond her, even this simple action drained her of strength. As though controlled by a nerve, his hand jerked and she thought he would pull away, deliberately cutting off the currents suddenly pulsing between them. He didn't. Suddenly he was cupping her face so painfully she almost cried out, but she stifled the sound before it escaped, afraid it might break the spell slowly binding them together.

She let her fingers slide to his wrist, giving a gentle tug. As he responded by sitting on the edge of the bed, she leaned towards him until they were only inches apart. Unable to stop trembling, she gazed at him silently, thinking it was just as well that her voice seemed frozen by the enormity of what she was doing. Otherwise, she might have been confessing wildly how much she loved him. As it was, there could be no exchange of words between them, for weren't tender murmurs of endearment only for those who shared a mutual love?

Carl, too, appeared curiously dumb, the blue of his eyes turning to black as they roamed slowly over her. Suddenly her fingers ached to touch the hardness of his face, the hard bones under his skin, to trace the uncompromising lines of jaw and chin. She stared, trance-like, at the strongly defined curve of his mouth, remembering how it had felt against her own, firm and cool, then demanding, hot and searching.

He made a sound in his throat. As always, he didn't want to touch her, but something was drawing him to her that he found impossible to resist. A great elation shook her as the iron bonds of his control broke and his arms came out to pull her close. Ripples of anticipation danced in a frightening sequence along her spine as his mouth came slowly towards her own.

To begin with he exercised restraint, and her racing heart warmed as she believed he was showing consideration. Then, feeling the tension in him, she realised that rather than thinking of her, he was still fighting his own rising desire. Gail felt him shudder and shuddered herself as heat began scorching through her. What she had experienced when he had kissed her previously had been nothing near as devastating as this.

Because she was still a virgin, she had no clear idea what it would be like to make love. She had a few vague notions, mostly picked up from odd things she'd heard and read, and tonight she had decided she would just have to take it one step at a time. She imagined there might be pleasure in it for the experienced, but for those with none, it might merely be something to be endured. Especially if, as in her case, it might be the only way she could keep her husband. The explosion of feeling that threatened to consume her now, as Carl caressed her gently and then began kissing her more insistently, was something she hadn't been prepared for.

His mouth lifted to trail over her cheek. She heard his voice, slightly roughened, in her ear. 'You realise what you're inviting, Gail?'

'I love you,' she whispered, unable to deny it.

'Shut up!' he cut in so brutally, he might have hit her. 'Women talk of love without having any idea of its true meaning. They use it as an excuse for abandoned behaviour while they don't really give a damn!'

A great unhappiness shook her. She had been wrong to mention love. It was no excuse that she hadn't meant to. She should have known it would touch a sore spot and Carl wouldn't believe her. Hadn't Petula Hogan shouted it from the rooftops? How many times had they heard her, at the stables, wrinkling her regal Roman nose while protesting gaily that, despite the horsy aroma, she loved him. No wonder Carl was now a bitter sceptic!

Something curled and tightened to a hard knot in Gail's stomach as she realised what she was up against, but she made herself go on. 'We aren't all the same, Carl.'

'So you keep telling me,' he said absently, as if he wasn't really concentrating on her reply. His brief anger seemed to have left him and his eyes were studying her mouth which felt suddenly very soft and vulnerable under his darkening gaze. His examination of her face was like a caress and she felt herself melting under the mounting heat of it into liquid fire flowing out to meet him, more than halfway.

She wasn't aware that she was going to speak until she heard her own voice. 'Perhaps you're right about some women, but I'm your wife, Carl.'

'And I'm not made of stone!' he retorted curtly, his hold tightening, this time with bruising force. Almost of their own volition, her arms wrapped round his neck as he kissed her with a hunger he didn't attempt to deny. He groaned deeply as he explored the responsive sweetness of her mouth. It was a sensual exploration and she couldn't seem to get enough of it. And, as his hands touched her breasts, she felt an incredible sensation spread to every corner of her body.

Swiftly he lowered her back on the bed, his hands becoming impatient with the satin and lace of her nightdress. He searched for a fastening, and on finding none, merely whipped the whole thing over her head. For a brief moment his ruthlessness jerked her back to reality, and as the lace tore she begged him to be careful.

'It can go in the drawer with the others,' he muttered indifferently.

'You know about them?' she gasped.

'I used to keep my socks in the same place,' he shrugged out of his short robe, throwing it after her nightdress on to the floor, 'but sometimes I forget.'

Gail was so busy following what he was saying, she forgot they were both naked. When she realised she gasped again with shock. The moonlight was thin, but even in semi-darkness, Carl, naked, seemed larger and much more dangerous than he had done before.

Fright rushed over her, but before she could move he grasped her again. 'Come here,' he said thickly, and suddenly she was lost. All her former fears and uncertainty were burned away by their mutual need.

Gail yielded as his mouth closed over her own and shivered as he slid half on top of her. This was all new to her. She could feel his rough body hair scraping her breasts and tried instinctively to put her hands between them as the feeling it aroused became unbearable. Carl didn't allow this, though. Instead he swept her hands out of the way while his own took possession of her stiffening nipples. Slipping slightly off her again, his mouth came down to join his hands, his tongue playing with the pink circles until they were completely distended.

She clung to him mindlessly, her heart hammering wildly as he dominated her every movement until she was caught up in the same primitive momentum as he was, helpless to deny the overwhelming force which was sweeping them rapidly along the path of no return. As his mouth crushed and kissed and bit relentlessly, it was like being caught in high winds on raging seas in a hurricane. There was no parallel she could draw like it. With a moan she gave herself up to the passionate emotions which were swiftly consuming her, suddenly revelling in their power and violence.

She was conscious of everything yet nothing. She could feel the urgency in Carl's body mounting as he gathered her closer. His hands began restlessly exploring the planes and curves of her back, then curved from the narrowness of her waist to the flatness of her stomach. He was strong, she was discovering, the muscles covering his body, hard and unyielding. His arms were like iron bands holding her to him, taking little account of the fragility of her own limbs.

Gail's breath began to quicken as their desire mounted and the ache in her pelvis began to grow unbearable. She felt a sense of desperate abandon which no matter how she tried to fight it only became greater. She could feel Carl's fingers caressing the delicate inner skin of her thigh and could hear herself mumbling but didn't know she was begging.

Her emotions were clearly beyond the point where it was possible to think of anything but his possession. When Carl parted her thighs and slid in between them she was far beyond being really conscious of what was happening. Her arms were round his shoulders, her hands buried in his thick hair, while her mouth sought his as fiercely as his had assaulted hers during the last ten minutes.

When she felt the thrust of his desire, like an invasion of fire, she felt a simultaneous tearing in her throat like a scream. She might have screamed again if the pressure of his mouth hadn't swiftly cut off her breath, and she lay waiting, quivering, while he remained where he was but didn't move. It was Gail who moved first, as some vital core of sensation deep inside her began stirring her frozen limbs. Soon the pain and apprehension disappeared and she was responding to exquisite pressures that sent surges of increasing pleasure searing right through her. She called out his name as a delirium of passion welded them together, but it wasn't enough. His mouth was on her breasts, but he made her wait, driving her almost mindless with impatience.

Then suddenly, unexpectedly, she was soaring upwards. She was joined to him, merging in rapture, as waves of shuddering sensation carried her higher and higher. Each new height seemed to bring a more maddening urgency, until suddenly, welded together, there came the final blinding release which left her tumbling into a stupor of half unconscious exhaustion. There was the weight of Carl collapsing abruptly across her, then she knew no more.

CHAPTER SIX

SOMETHING woke her—some movement or sound, perhaps merely the faint breeze from the open window, she could feel on her face. Then she saw Carl, standing a little way from the bed, staring down at her. What was he doing? How long had he been there? Gail blinked, her eyes heavy from sleep, nothing of what had happened through the night registering immediately,

She felt strangely tired, her body languid, then she remembered. Carl had slept with her in this bed. He had made love to her, accepting her as his wife at last. There was the memory of pleasure and pain, all of it somewhat unreal in the harsh light of day, but that Carl was here was proof that this wasn't an ordinary morning. Always before he had been gone, no matter how early she woke.

He was dressed, a sweater pulled over an open-necked shirt, his face cool and remote. The coolness in his eyes contained a certain wariness. He was gazing at her as if he was determined that the intimacy of a few hours ago shouldn't be allowed to continue.

'Good morning,' she breathed uncertainly,

He stiffened and she wondered if he had just realised she was awake, yet if his thoughts hadn't been with her, where had they been?

'Good morning,' he said curtly,

'What time is it?' she asked slowly, suddenly wishing desperately that he hadn't been there when she woke, so that she could have had time to get her thoughts sorted out.

'Nine-thirty,' he answered abruptly.

'Nine-thirty!' Dismayed, she began to jump out of bed, then realised she had nothing on. 'Oh!' She pulled the sheet up again, over her tender breasts, her cheeks hot. 'You shouldn't have let me sleep in. I've never done such a thing!'

'Another record broken,' he said mockingly.

She gazed at him, her nerves tightening, her heart pounding, quite aware of what he was implying. His scathing glance was hinting at other things too. After last night it was pointless to huddle under the bedclothes. He didn't seem to understand that it wasn't easy to discard the reticence of a perhaps too sheltered upbringing all at once. Especially when the atmosphere wasn't exactly encouraging.

'What about the yard?' she asked quickly. Dick Noble wouldn't have arrived yet.

'All taken care of,' Carl assured her impatiently, 'There's no need to worry.' He hesitated, as if mulling over something he had conceded to against his better judgment. 'I told Frank you could do the rounds this evening. I believe he has a date.'

Her radiant smile appeared to startle him. He sat down on the edge of the bed, without taking his eyes off her. 'Does the yard mean so much to you, Gail?'

It wasn't that. He could easily have arranged for someone else to do the rounds. She had felt happy because she'd thought he had been considering her, but the sudden harshness in his voice prevented her from trying to explain. If he had kissed her, this morning, she might have been able to, but how could she when he was gazing at her so impersonally?

'Yes and no,' she said hesitantly, as he was obviously about to repeat his question. 'Having to leave the yard is something I'll have to get used to.' Her green eyes, huge in her anxious face, begged unconsciously for understanding. 'I will eventually, I expect. There must be plenty to do here—if you'll let me help?'

It was half query, half a suggestion, and she waited tensely for his comment.

She was startled when he laughed, though she wasn't sure if he was amused. 'You're a funny girl, Gail.' Derisively his glance went over her, noting the bare, enticing outlines of her slender body under the sheet. 'You've just gone through probably the most shattering experience in your life, yet all you can think of is horses!'

That's not true! she was about to protest, but stopped herself in time. Horses were important to her, but they never dominated her thoughts as Carl did. She would much rather have talked about what had happened last night, but she dared not even mention it for fear he believed she was pestering him for promises of fidelity. If she angered him, he was quite capable of disappearing for weeks, and she daren't risk that!

'You haven't told me if I can help you,' she hedged, ignoring his remarks as the only thing she could do.

'Do what you like,' he shrugged, 'as long as you don't get in my way.'

'There's not much fear of that,' she muttered. 'You generally make sure I keep out of it.'

He smiled softly. 'You don't have to keep out of it all the time. Last night I had no complaints.'

Did he mean last night, or through the night? 'I'd like to get up,' she said unevenly. If she didn't, whatever he meant, she might be in danger of begging him to make love to her again. Already she could feel a stirring of desire warming her traitorous flesh.

'I'm not stopping you,' Carl replied blandly.

She moved, then winced, her breath drawn sharply.

'Are you all right?' His eyes were immediately alert on her pale face.

'Yes.' Biting her lip, she looked determinedly away from his disturbing masculinity. Despite the soreness of her limbs, she knew a feverish longing to throw herself at him. She wanted to feel his arms round her and hear his voice commanding her to forget everything for the next few hours. Terribly ashamed of her own wantonness, which she had never suspected before, she blushed and positively hung her head.

'Are you sure?' he persisted.

When she nodded dumbly, he laid a hand on her

shoulder, curving the warm skin over fragile bones. Then his fingers slipped to her neck, his thumb under her chin, raising it to study the heat in her cheeks, the sweet, tremulous softness of her mouth. His head lowered with excruciating slowness towards her and she felt again the odd sensation of melting into him as she closed her eyes.

'Gail?' he said thickly, pausing but a hair's breadth from her lips. Then the telephone rang beside them.

With a smothered curse, Carl let go of her and reached for it, for the next minute or so having a brief conversation with his manager.

'Got to go,' he said briefly, without explaining why, but Gail gathered a minor crisis had blown up. He might have been going to kiss her, but he didn't appear despondent that he had been interrupted.

'What's wrong?' she asked quickly, as he jumped to his feet.

'Nothing much.'

He didn't want to discuss it. Already he was shutting her out. 'Then why can't Neil deal with it?'

Carl turned at the door, ignoring her question. 'I'd have a warm bath, if I were you. Don't overdo things. Mavis is busy clearing up, so there's nothing to worry about. We don't have to be at the Grange until one.'

Carl didn't return until twelve-thirty and he changed hurriedly. His hair was still damp from the shower as they drove to his uncle's place, but as usual, he looked immaculate. Glancing at him sideways, Gail wondered how he did it. No one would ever believe he had been covered with dust and grime half an hour ago. Yet even when hot and dusty, he was so tall and broad-shouldered, he seemed to have a kind of presence not given to many men.

One of the horses had managed to get through a fence surrounding a swamp and sunk up to its belly. It had been the devil of a job, getting him out but fortunately the colt wasn't much the worse for his experience.

'If I'd known, I could have been there,' Gail said resentfully, when Carl explained what had kept him.

'That's why I didn't tell you,' he replied briefly, 'otherwise you might not have been fit to go out to lunch.'

She had accepted his explanation—or excuse, whichever it was—without saying anything more, but she still had the feeling he was shutting her out.

The Grange, the home of Sir Arthur and Lady Elliot, was a pleasant house about twelve miles away. Gail had passed it many times, but this was the first time she had actually been there. She wondered if Grace would be at home. Her parents were quite pleasant, but Grace, with her constant flow of malicious hints and digs, wasn't exactly Gail's favourite person!

She glanced at Carl again, her attention never willing to wander from him for long. In linen pants and jacket, with a toning shirt, he looked striking. He took her breath away, and suddenly she wished they could have been going somewhere on their own, so she didn't have to share him with anybody, not even his relations.

Feeling her eyes on him, he turned his head. 'Not worried about going to Arthur's, are you?'

She assured him she wasn't.

Carl sighed. 'There's likely to be a houseful of guests, he tends to invite people indiscriminately. If the place is crowded out, I hope you won't mind.'

She shook her head with a smile. 'Grace is the only one I might feel like running a mile from. I don't think she approves of me.'

'She'd better change her tune,' he said grimly. 'Anyway, I'll be around.'

Gail didn't, for one moment, imagine he was thinking of her personally. She was a chattel, something belonging to him, and a man's possessions were often as much a matter of pride as affection. She wouldn't delude herself that she mattered more to him now than she had done yesterday. Letting him—no, she had to be honest, tempting him to make love to her had been a mistake, one which mustn't be repeated. She had been wrong, terribly wrong, she realised bleakly, crossing her arms tightly round her waist as her body began to tremble. She had used sex merely as a means to an end, and Carl would be quite right if he thought her devious and calculating. He might pretend in public, for the sake of appearances to be fond of her, but she guessed that his opinion of her was probably lower than ever.

Feeling full of remorse, she put a hand on his thigh, without realising what she was doing. 'Carl,' she began, 'about last night . . .'

His glance flicked to her hand and, flushing bright red, she snatched it away. 'I'm sorry.'

'What about?' he asked curtly. 'Sleeping with me or touching me?'

'B-both!' she gasped.

'Interesting,' he snapped. 'Was it something I said that brought this on?'

'No, of course not,' she protested quickly, 'but I've scarcely seen you this morning, and I realise last night was—well, my fault.'

His laughter was harsh. 'I'm not complaining!'

Gail swallowed, never having been so relieved in her life when the Grange loomed in view. The conversation was closed, for good, if the look on Carl's face was anything to go by, without having been brought to any satisfactory conclusion. She felt so covered with confusion she wished the ground would open and swallow her up!

As they walked across the drive after parking the car, there seemed to be a dreadful silence between them. She asked, more because she couldn't endure it than that she really wanted to know, 'Do I look all right?'

'Yes.' His eyes rested on her without any real interest.

'Thanks,' she whispered.

Something about her slightly woeful expression must have touched a chord of remorse. 'Oh, God!' he muttered. 'I'm sorry, Gail. I seem to have acquired the knack of hurting you. I should never have married you in the first place.'

Gail went white, but the anger she felt saved her, at least from bursting into tears and making a fool of herself. Was he trying to comfort or kill her? It wasn't the first time he had expressed his regrets regarding their marriage, but she did wish he hadn't mentioned it today. Just when she needed extra confidence, he seemed to have removed what little she had.

'You can always get a divorce,' she said bitterly, as the butler let them in. 'If you want one,' she went on, when the grasp of Carl's steely fingers made her realise he was trying to warn her of something. Too late, she saw Grace standing directly inside the front door. Grace had obviously overheard every word she had been saying and looked like a cat with a saucer of cream.

'Not quarrelling already?' she asked sweetly.

When Gail didn't reply and Carl merely glanced at her coldly, she slipped an arm through his. 'Felicity's here. When she heard you were coming, she invited herself as well. And she's brought half the cast from the new show she's in with her! I know you're going to enjoy meeting them, darling.'

'What makes you think so?' he said dryly, freeing his arm.

'Perhaps the way you were fighting with your wife?' she said lightly. 'I remembered Felicity saying the last time she saw you in London, you weren't getting on very well.'

Sir Arthur, charging from the drawing room, was a welcome diversion, but under cover of his jovial greetings, Grace managed to whisper to Gail, 'She also said that Carl had told her that himself, while they were having lunch together.'

Whether this was true or not, Gail couldn't be sure, but it did seem that he hadn't been wholly honest with her regarding Felicity. He must have taken her to lunch as well as tea, that day in the hotel, and he could have been seeing her at other times as well. He was in love with Petula, but if that didn't prevent him making love to his wife, he must find it just as easy to make love to other women?

Felicity, though, if she did imagine she had some position in Carl's life and was determined to strengthen it, didn't obviously appear to be succeeding. During the afternoon he rarely left Gail's side, making her begin to wonder if she had misjudged him. He even sat beside her in the drawing-room when coffee was served, putting an arm possessively around her making Felicity look decidedly put out. As did the bunch of bright young women she had brought with her. There was a decided lack of male company, and though Sir Arthur and one or two others did their gallant best, Gail wasn't sure their efforts were appreciated.

They left at four to return to Deanly, after Carl refused to stay for tea. He surprised her by suggesting they should call on Ruth and Donald on their way home, something which had never seemed to occur to him before.

Gail thought about it, but decided it wasn't such a good idea, not on a Sunday. 'I think,' she said carefully, 'by the time we got there, Donald would be leaving for evening service.'

'And you have your rounds.'

'For the last time,' she reminded him.

He nodded, then asked if she would like to go for a short run, as she didn't need to be back until six, at the earliest. This time she agreed. Carl hadn't wanted to stay longer at the Grange, nor was he apparently keen to go straight home. He was oddly restless.

'I thought we might ask Ruth and Donald to dinner one evening,' she said tentatively, as he turned out of his uncle's drive, in the opposite direction to Deanly. 'They're moving to the south coast in a fortnight, remember I told you? which won't be so convenient for visiting.'

'Yes, by all means,' he said absently, 'ask anyone you like.'

Gail sighed, recognising his mood. He was not only restless but bored.

'We didn't have to rush away from the Grange,' she said tensely. 'You mightn't have been so keen to leave if you'd circulated more.'

'What's that supposed to mean?' he snapped.

'I don't know,' she confessed unhappily, not looking at him, 'but you didn't have to stay with me all the time.'

'Maybe it was safer.'

'Safer?'

His mouth twisted cynically. 'Women on their own can be deadly, but when they're hunting in packs a man mightn't stand a chance.'

She didn't believe he was altogether serious but couldn't help retorting shortly, 'I'm not sure about the others, but Felicity looked as if she could have eaten you alive!'

'Which isn't my fault,' he rejoined.

'You must have encouraged her!'

'I beg your pardon!'

How did one continue in such an icy atmosphere? With an effort, Gail moved frozen lips. 'You must have realised what you were doing when you took her out,' she began, only to be cut off by a voice like a whip.

'You surely didn't believe all that guff Grace was spouting? That bit about lunch might have been what Felicity had told her but it could have been made up by either of them. I've never taken the woman anywhere, and it's nice to know how much you trust me!'

'But you did have tea with her!'

'In circumstances I've already explained. But my marriage—our marriage, was never even mentioned.'

Unhappily, Gail bit her lip. 'It's not really a case of trust,' she said, after a minute.

He gave her a frosty look. 'Then I'd like to know what it is.'

Gail swallowed away some restriction in her throat. 'You—you made love to me, and I thought . . .'

Carl broke in sharply. 'You thought any woman would do?'

'Am I far wrong?' she asked painfully. 'I'm no expert on these matters . . .'

Again he cut in. 'Then I suggest you leave it to those who are.'

'I'm sorry,' she whispered, wondering where was the reassurance his words should bring. At this moment she could only find pain, going through her body in ever widening circles. She had to fight desperately to keep the pain from her eyes so he wouldn't see it. If he knew how much she loved him, he might understand how she couldn't dismiss her fears and doubts so easily. But she couldn't tell him. She had tried to tell him last night and he had merely been angry.

Sunk in thought, undisturbed this time by the taut silence between them, she wasn't aware that he had pulled off the road until he actually stopped.

'Look, Gail,' he said suddenly, turning her grimly towards him, studying the paleness of her face, 'we may or may not have been wise to get married, but until now I've been a faithful husband. And, as long as we're married, I'll go on being one. When—if the day comes when I decide we'd be better apart, I'll tell you so, but as long as we're together, you don't have to worry about other women. And that's a promise.'

Gail felt tears spring to her eyes and immediately felt very humble. Carl might never be easy to live with, but his word was his bond. She would never doubt it.

'I'd like to make a promise too,' she said tremulously. 'I love you and I'll try and make you a good wife. For as long as you need me,' she added hastily, sensing rather than seeing the frown in his eyes. 'I—you know I'd never stand in the way of your true happiness, should you ever get another chance.'

She could sense the different emotions running through him while she spoke, his distaste when she mentioned loving him, the indrawn hardness of his breath when she had alluded to Petula. There was a flare of hostility towards her that she had reminded him of something he would rather forget, but some things had to be said, there was no other way.

She could read nothing from his face. It was like a mask when she looked at him, and tears came to her eyes. Didn't he realise, she knew as well as he did the anguish of loving someone who didn't love one in return?

'I didn't mean to hurt you,' she sighed tearfully, leaning towards him, laying a gentle hand on his arm, this time not caring if he objected or not. It seemed much more important that he should know she understood.

With a groan, he suddenly gathered her to him, lifting her mouth to kiss her almost tenderly. 'I'm not hurt,' he said slowly, 'but I'd hate you to be.'

He kissed her again, which he probably intended to be a brief way of indicating the subject was closed, but somehow their lips began to cling. Instead of putting her from him, his arms were around her and he was kissing her throat and her cheeks as well as her lips. He began holding her so close she couldn't breathe,

Then suddenly he drew back and she saw his jaw tighten. He said nothing for a moment, his eyes brooding, and a peculiar tension seemed to exist between them until he broke it by exclaiming wryly. 'You're getting to be too kissable, young lady!'

Gail even managed a light laugh, though her heart was galloping out of control. 'Is that a crime?'

'Not when your husband's around,' he returned, 'unless you get too attractive for my peace of mind.'

He smiled teasingly, obviously making an effort, as she was, to ease the tautness between them, and she tried to respond. 'I've been working on improving my image—but perhaps I'd better stop?'

The teasing smile faded from his face and his eyes were suddenly intent. 'I noticed how beautiful you are during lunch. I don't know how I ever thought of you as plain.'

'Oh, Carl,' she laughed, not really fishing for compliments, 'I can't have changed that much!'

'No, you haven't,' he retorted, almost curtly. 'Bone structure, fundamental beauty can't be altered. You've merely done something to make me realise it's there.'

It ought to have been a moment of sweet triumph. It would have been if only Carl had loved her. She forced another smile. 'I've been learning a little about dressing and how to apply make-up properly,' she explained.

He nodded, not bothering to conceal the admiration in his eyes. 'No wonder poor Jeff got carried away! I'll probably have to hide you, next time he arrives.'

'Do you think I'm likely to desert you?'

'You'd better not,' he growled, but she had no means of knowing if he was serious.

They drove on, meandering through Inkpen and Combe, the latter a lonely, tree-shaded village between three enormous downs. There were glorious views of the Kennet Valley from the downs and the rolling expanses of countryside were green with growing corn.

'I never tire of the English countryside,' Carl said softly. 'Every time I go abroad, the thing I enjoy most about my trip is coming back to it. I've often considered the advantages of living abroad, but I guess this is where my heart is.'

'Have you ever been away from Deanly for long?' Gail asked, for she didn't know a lot about what really mattered to him.

'Just at boarding school. I hated that,' he said ruefully. 'I found university much more of a challenge. You never appreciate the advantages of education, though, until you're my age.'

'I hated boarding school too,' she confessed. 'It was Lady Purdie's fault really. She disliked having children under her feet, and insisted I went to one. She and Dad argued about it, but Dad gave in.'

Carl grinned sympathetically. 'I remember you were just finishing when Sean came to me. I used to think you were a nuisance too—constantly about the stables, all long legs and wide eyes. It still surprises me that you aren't very tall. But you could ride a horse like the wind. You were a joy to watch, so I always forgave you.'

Carl's compliments were going to her head, she felt dazed with pleasure. She was amazed that he had noticed her at all. Over the years, his censure, like Lady Purdie's, was something she had grown used to, and she was startled to discover he had admired her in any way.

'I've always loved riding,' she said.

He turned his head to glance at her thoughtfully. 'You should have had proper equestrian training. There's still time and you could do well. Show jumping's another possibility too, though some of the jumps are getting so high I don't know if my nerves would stand seeing you risking your neck!'

Gail pretended to be considering what he said. Only a few weeks ago she might have seized such a chance, but now she wasn't so sure. Perhaps, like Carl, she was changing, coming to realise what was important—to her anyway. She knew the sheer hard work, the long hours which went into any kind of specialised horsemanship, and, even if she could afford it, she wasn't sure that this was the direction she wanted her life to take. If there was any chance of her marriage succeeding, she would much rather devote her time to looking after Carl and bringing up his children. She couldn't tell him that, of course, as he would merely feel trapped instead of pleased. She sighed wistfully for the many things she thought of each day and daren't mention for fear of embàrrassing him.

Choosing her words carefully, she said, 'I think I'll take a break for a while and see how it goes. There's the house to sort out and you've asked me long enough about finding a housekeeper.'

He didn't say anything when she talked of taking a break, but he frowned when she mentioned a housekeeper. 'Must we?' he asked. 'I'll admit I've grown to like having more privacy. My grandmother had so many servants they were in constant danger of falling over each other, and my mother would have been as bad if times hadn't changed. As it was, she had her share!'

Gail felt almost as curious about his parents as she did over him. 'Didn't your mother enjoy doing things about the house herself?' she asked tentatively.

'Not so you'd notice,' he shrugged. 'She was forty when I was born and she liked to believe her health was never the same afterwards, although I was assured by her doctor that I had nothing to do with it. She and my father didn't get on and she merely suffered from nerves and restlessness.'

It shocked Gail that a man could be so cynical about his own mother, yet she realised there must be a reason for it. Pushed off to boarding school before he was eight, and holidays spent with parents constantly quarrelling, must have made him wary regarding human relationships long before he was grown up. Perhaps that was why he had waited until he was thirty-six before allowing himself to fall in love? Now Gail felt she could see why he was so terribly bitter about Petula leaving him.

'Your mother must have died young,' she said quietly, without referring to anything else.

'Yes,' he said shortly. 'She was seventy. My father was older.'

By tacit agreement they didn't mention his parents again as they returned to Deanly but discussed only the passing countryside and the possibility of employing casual staff who would come in for a few hours each day, or longer when they were entertaining. It was just after six when they got back, and Gail changed quickly and went straight out again. Later, just as she was finishing at the stables, she was surprised to see Carl approaching.

'I thought we could take two of the horses out for an hour?' he suggested. 'I know you've been busy here but I've done little else but sit all afternoon. You don't have to come though, if you'd rather not.'

The thought of riding through the cool of the evening

with Carl filled her with pleasure, yet he hadn't had anything to eat for hours and he must be hungry.

'What about dinner?' she asked uncertainly.

'We can get something later,' he said, adding dryly, 'After that lunch at the Grange, I think we could probably manage on toast and boiled eggs.'

Carl said an hour, but dusk was falling when they returned. Gail enjoyed herself, but by the time they got back she was almost falling asleep in the saddle. When Carl lifted her from her horse to the ground, she could have laid her head against his broad chest and left it there.

If Carl had lapsed into one of his black moods again, she was too weary to notice. It wasn't until they had nearly finished the light supper she made that she became aware of the grimness of his face.

'Is—there anything wrong?' she asked anxiously.

'Nothing at all,' he drawled curtly, getting to his feet. 'Perhaps, like you, I'm feeling rather tired, but I have some paper work to do before I turn in.'

She began gathering up the dishes. 'I'll just do these, then, while you're busy.'

'Please yourself,' he replied abruptly, on his way out. 'But don't wait up, I'm not sure when I'll be through.'

When his study door banged in the distance, Gail suddenly knew she mightn't see him again that night. He had scarcely spoken two words while they had been out riding, or during supper, and she feared he was retreating from her again.

Flushing painfully, she washed the dishes, letting the water run warmly over her hands. Last night she had almost thrown herself at him, and obviously he didn't want a repeat performance. Rather than risk it, he would sleep downstairs. He must have taken her riding deliberately, to avoid being alone with her in the house, and, as she realised this, her cheeks burned with humiliation.

The tears in her eyes made everything a blur and she stayed in the kitchen until she had control of herself.

Didn't he understand that she was trying to help him, that she wanted to help him, and that he might be hurting both of them by shutting her out? How could anyone be so cruel, so cold and insensitive? This afternoon she had believed they could be happy together. Now she was convinced that that was an impossible dream!

Then she calmed down as the sequence of the previous night reeled past her vision. How could she expect a man like Carl Elliot to love her if she acted like a child? Last night he had taken what she had offered, and if he was regretting what had happened, it might be more for her sake than his own. Putting a little distance between them, might simply be his way of giving her time to be sure of her own feelings. And, if she loved him, perhaps she should be willing to give him some time too?

Feeling more composed, she went upstairs to bed. Removing her clothes, she had a shower before putting on her old cotton pyjamas and getting into bed. Uncertainly, she looked at Carl's larger one, but decided to stay where she was. If he wanted her there, she couldn't do more than she had done to prove she was willing to share it. Now it was up to him.

The wind was rising, blowing directly through the open window on her face. She liked fresh air, but not that much! With an impatient sigh she tumbled out of bed to close it. The garden was bathed in moonlight and for a moment she stood watching shadows, tossed by the wind from the trees and thrown across the lawn. A flash of lightning lit the sky, followed by a distant rumble of thunder, and she sighed for the fickleness of English weather. The day and evening had been dry and hot, now a storm was brewing.

A sound by the door made her turn sharply. It was Carl. He came in and closed the door. She stared at him over the moonlit room, her eyes wide with surprise. He was wearing his usual short bath robe, which he must have collected while she showered, because she hadn't heard him. He was watching her, but she could see nothing but the cold glitter of his eyes. They were oddly menacing. She was reminded of a night animal stalking its prey, or a man seeking vengeance.

He came nearer slowly and she saw she hadn't been wrong. There was nothing in his face but cold desire, no hate but no love. Just sheer, burning need, over which he was exercising little control.

Wordlessly she stared at him. Where were his promises of the afternoon? Then she realised that the things he had promised had nothing to do with the feelings burning through him now. He had promised to be faithful, not that he wouldn't hurt her. His treatment of her hadn't been discussed. He had just said he wouldn't have an affair with another women while they were together.

Gail stood, neither moving nor speaking. She fought desperately to keep her eyes steady as he paused beside her. She could feel him assessing her reactions to his presence and she was determined to issue no invitation, either verbally or otherwise. A treacherous heat began spreading through her which she did her best to suppress. If he hadn't been so tall and attractive, she might have managed better, but she couldn't completely stop herself from responding to his undoubted masculinity.

'I thought you were working?' she said jerkily when he remained silent. When it came to a battle of nerves, he had to be the winner! Because of this her voice was bitter.

'I followed you up.'

He must have done, but why? Gail began to tremble and he watched her closely. Seeing the flicker of fear in her eyes, his own narrowed with satisfaction. When she said nothing more, he asked coolly, 'Why aren't you in bed?'

'I was.'

'Couldn't you sleep?' again came the gleam of satisfaction.

She backed away from it, pushing agitated fingers through her tumbled hair. 'The window was open and the wind's getting up.' The blue eyes taunted her mockingly and suddenly she didn't care about the weather, or what he thought! 'What do you want, Carl?' she cried miserably.

'A welcome, perhaps.' A dark brow lifted derisively, 'Am I welcome, Gail?'

CHAPTER SEVEN

GAIL stepped back in alarm, knowing what he was asking. The strong, dark planes of his face held a remorseless determination. He had asked a question, but there was only one answer he would accept. He might appear to be giving her a choice, but he wasn't. Last night he had fought the attraction between them so obviously that she had vowed the next move must come from him, but now that it had, she was terrified. Last night she had managed to survive a whirlwind, but further exposure might leave her devastated. When she had begged Carl to make love to her, she hadn't known what she was inviting, and that, she suspected, shivering, had only been the beginning.

The tension in her was so strong she was shaking with it. She stared at him, her eyes pleading, but he merely smiled with barbed amusement. 'Where's all the courage you displayed twenty-four hours ago? The loving you promised this afternoon? Perhaps we should have got it down on paper? Drawn all the demarcation lines?'

She hung her head miserably. She deserved his censure, but he wasn't exactly encouraging. There was a need in him which had nothing to do with love, and she had no time to discover what it was. Words like revenge and hate flickered through her mind, to be dismissed as ridiculous. Carl couldn't possibly hate her, could he? Not after everything she had done for him.

Yet if it wasn't hate there was something very near it in the cruel grip of the hands which caught her long hair, dragging her to him. 'If the cat's got your tongue,' he snapped, as she cried out in pain, 'maybe this will help?'

Gail tried to escape, quivering from head to foot as

113

he forcibly pulled her closer. The violence in him froze
her voice solid, so she had to moisten her lips before she
could speak. 'You don't have to be so angry,' she
choked. 'You startled me. I thought you were
downstairs, but I meant what I said this afternoon.'

Carl muttered something under his breath as his
mouth swooped demandingly. Whatever his reply, he
wasn't giving her a chance to change her mind. He
kissed her deeply, and so pitilessly he made her gasp.
She could taste the salt of her own blood on her tongue
and frantically tried to push him away.

He didn't budge an inch. Her indignant hands
encountered solid flesh as immovable as the stone walls
around her. Lifting her struggling body, he carried her
to the bed. In a trice he had them both naked and was
lying beside her.

For a few moments he lay breathing harshly but
holding her still. Then, without warning he resumed his
brutal attack on her mouth. She could feel the anger in
him expressing itself through the force he used and she
quivered. When he released her lips they felt quite numb
and she whispered tearfully, 'You hurt me!'

'I meant to, you two-timing little bitch,' he said
roughly. 'Despite your fine promises, you're all the
same.'

'I told you, I meant what I said this afternoon,' she
protested huskily. 'I love you.'

'I don't want your love!' he retorted savagely. 'I never
asked for it, or encouraged it, so don't blame me if you
get hurt.'

'Don't you care at all?' she gulped.

'If I care,' he rapped, 'it's because you're my wife,
something belonging to me, but not for you personally.'

Gail felt cold and miserable, yet he was only spelling
out what she already knew. She trembled as he ran
insolent eyes down her naked body and her face flamed
then went like ice. He moved half over her, grinding his
chest over her sensitive breasts. The blood raced to her
head and as she gasped she saw the triumph in his eyes.

Taking a deep breath, she prayed for better understanding. Carl must still be hurting terribly, to be capable of saying such things. Tenderness and sympathy overwhelmed her. If she cared for him her love might act like a healing balm and he might forget. Even now, when he thought he hated her, he went on holding her. He wasn't exactly pushing her away!

Trying to accept their nakedness without a qualm, she wrapped her arms round him and gently kissed his cheek. Immediately he turned his head and covered her mouth with the now familiar flare of urgency which she sensed surprised him as much as it did her. He forced her lips apart, probing them warmly, so that she melted helplessly into a sensuous response, kissing him back hotly.

She trembled, responding passionately, her senses aflame. She felt his hot caresses on her eyes and ears and neck, and his arms locking her tightly to him. He eased slightly back to let his hands slide downwards over the taut planes of her stomach to her hips and the silky firmness of her thighs, and she became a quivering mass of sensation with her stomach twisting into knots. He seemed intent on driving her a little more frantic with every movement he made.

Her own hands gripped and moved on his broad shoulders, feeling the tenseness of his muscles. His back was bare, his skin hot with desire. Being able to touch him like this filled her with excitement, bringing small, animal-like whimpers to her throat. Fleetingly she wondered why he couldn't love her as she loved him, then all this would have been perfect.

As though he was aware of her changing mood, the pressure of his hands increased and her regrets dissolved before a fierce rush of pleasure. She moaned as his lips caressed her throat, trailing a path of fire down its creamy length to the soft, shadowed cleft between her breasts. When his teeth closed over first one rose-tipped mound and then the other, she imagined her last shreds of sanity were disappearing.

'Carl . . .' she whispered, through lips swollen from his kisses.

'Touch me,' he said thickly, taking her hand and laying it where she could feel his heart thudding against her palm. His eyes devoured her and her lashes fell before the flames in their blue depth.

His mouth claimed hers again and she felt him shudder as her hands drifted over him, moist with the dampness of sweat from his shoulders and chest. He was gripping her tightly, but she was on fire for him, willing to endure any pain he might inflict as a small price to pay for the pleasure he could give her. There was a wild singing in her ears and head which was swiftly removing any sense of reality.

She began floating, scarcely aware, as her body went fluid, of Carl lifting her slightly towards him as her slender legs entangled with his, as the weight of his body pressed her down on the bed. He had been silent until now, but as he possessed her he breathed her name hoarsely, as though it was dragged from him. When his control went, his invasion of her wasn't gentle, but with her own senses flaming Gail didn't need his gentleness. Often she might, but at this moment she responded eagerly to the growing heat of his desire, letting it consume her. Passionately she clung to him, her whole being throbbing with the need for release which he eventually gave her. She might have had no separate entity of her own, so completely did her every movement match his, and when together they reached the same incredible heights they had attained the night before she knew, among other things, a great sense of awe and wonder.

Carl lay still beside her. She had a great longing to hear him speak to her, even just a few words, but he didn't. There was a darkness in his eyes and dull coins of colour in his cheeks and his mouth was clamped shut. His arm was round her and he didn't remove it, and she felt bewildered that he still appeared to be angry. Surely what had happened between them should have brought a sense of peace, even if he didn't love her? Or was it that he secretly resented wanting her and the satisfaction it had given him? She had felt his muscles wrench as they had reached the peak of sensation in the same second, and heard his hoarse, rasping gasp, which had seemed to contain incredulous surprise as well as pleasure. Was he surprised, perhaps, that they were so compatible?

She was tired and knew a desire for sleep, yet she could feel something stronger stirring inside her. Flushing deeply she turned away, refusing to credit her own instinctive sensuality. How could every part of her be crying out for him when he had just taken her so ruthlessly and couldn't even spare her a kind word?

She tried to move to the other side of the bed, but he wouldn't let her go. 'I want you again,' he said thickly, pulling her back to him with a look that threatened violence, should she try and escape.

Despite the instant response of her body, she had to protest. 'You'll hate me tomorrow, Carl!'

'Why worry about tomorrow when we can enjoy ourselves tonight?' he said huskily, repossessing her mouth with hungry lips and beginning to make love to her again.

Next morning Carl was sleeping as she crept out of bed. It was very early and although she was used to rising at such an hour, today she didn't feel like getting up at all. She looked with longing down on Carl's strong body. He was lying on his face, the sheet just covering the hard curve of his powerful hips, his back and shoulders bare. Gail swallowed as she remembered how his skin had felt under her clinging hands. They seemed only just to have fallen asleep. Carl had proved an insatiable lover and she had been more than ready to meet his every demand. This morning, as she gazed at him, she was full of doubts. She could be giving too much of herself. He didn't really appreciate her and would probably only despise her for inciting his emotions.

She had decided to go out on the early morning gallop. Frank would be there, but he would welcome her, she knew. They had a horse entered for Ascot which was one of the greatest—Gail considered the greatest—race meetings of the year. She hadn't discussed it yet with Carl, but she was greatly looking forward to accompanying him there as his wife. At Newmarket she had been apprehensive, but as her fears had proved groundless, she was looking forward to Ascot with no such inhibitions on her mind.

Managing to dress without disturbing Carl, she crept from the house. The air was fresh and clean after the rain that had preceded the overnight storm, though the apple and cherry blossom, late this year, lay on the ground like snow, scattered by the wind. The horse, Dinkum, was on rare form, showing the rest of the field a pair of clean heels. It didn't take a lot of imagination to see him, wearing Carl's colours, coming in first. Next year, if Dinkum went on improving, he might even win the Gold Cup. It wouldn't be the first big race they had won.

Gail felt almost happy as she returned to the house at eight o'clock. Like Carl, she appreciated the flexibility of being on their own. Though she tried to keep to a regular routine over their meals, they didn't have to worry about them. Carl having obviously gone out himself, she began preparing breakfast. He wouldn't have eaten yet, and at breakfast time, especially, he was always hungry. Thinking of his appetite for other things, she was grateful for being young enough to respond to him without being exhausted. He was virile enough for two, she realised, and was thankful that she loved him and was able to return his ardour with a passion that seemed to satisfy him.

Hearing him come in, she glanced up from the toaster with a shy smile which he ignored. She was so used to having him scowling at her that she wasn't unduly disturbed until he spoke. Then it was his tone which alarmed her.

'Where have you been?' he snapped.

'Oh, just seeing Dinkum run,' she found herself almost apologising. 'I didn't think you'd mind.'

'Next time ask me!' he shot back, clearly in a filthy mood.

'You were asleep . . .' she explained.

Whose fault is that? his eyes seemed to say, before he turned his back on her to wash his hands at the sink.

Feeling scorched by his furious glance, Gail flushed unhappily. She had expected Carl might take her in his arms and kiss her, this morning, but nothing was turning out as she had expected. Then she wondered if he was cross because she hadn't stayed in bed. How could she explain that she had wanted to, but had been too afraid that if she did she might be in danger of betraying too much of herself? Carl didn't want her telling him how much she loved him, but she didn't find it easy to remain as silent as he did.

The towel was missing and while she searched for one he snapped over his shoulder. 'There wasn't any point in your going out. Dick Noble will be here today.'

'I know that!' she replied, more tensely than she might have done if she hadn't felt so overwrought.

'Then why did you?' he persisted.

He was like a dog with a bone. No, more like a wolf with a lamb! she corrected herself angrily. 'Just because you've a trainer coming—at last!' she emphasised sharply, 'surely that doesn't mean I can't go out with the horses any more? After all, I have helped to train Dinkum to the stage where he's ready for Ascot.'

'Ascot!'

His eyes weren't merely scorching now, they were annihilating. He had peculiar eyes. When he was emotionally moved they went darker, but when he was angry they took on the silvery sheen of ice. Gail glanced at him quickly, then away again, unable to sustain the coldness of his gaze. 'You can't have forgotten?' she mumbled uncertainly.

'I haven't forgotten Ascot,' he said clearly, as

though speaking to a child, 'but we won't be going this year.'

'Not—going?'

'I've withdrawn Dinkum—I've just told Frank. He's sold. Gordon Dilston's wanted him long enough. I've told him he can have him.'

Withdrawn—sold! Gail was so stunned she was spluttering, 'But you can't have done! What for . . .?'

That she wasn't willing to accept what he said without question, infuriated him. Grasping her swiftly, he gave her a rough little shake. 'Listen to me, Gail, and I won't repeat myself again. The stables are to be run down, then closed. And if you say to me—you can't, just once more, so help me, I'll strangle you!'

'It's not that!' Suddenly she was frantic. 'I know you intend closing the stables down, but you said gradually. What's wrong with Dinkum running? It's all arranged.'

'Was.'

'You mean you really have withdrawn him? You're not just saying it because I disobeyed you this morning?'

'You can ring Gordon up if you like and check.'

A cold chill ran down her spine that he could be so ruthless. She shook her head in a mute, negative rush of feeling, her throat working convulsively.

Carl watched the distress on her face for a long moment before saying curtly, 'You've never really accepted my decision about stopping training, have you, Gail? You have our winners all lined up in your tenacious little mind, planning greater things for them in the future.'

It was so near the truth, her eyes widened and she flushed with guilt. Yet she hadn't been doing it consciously. She might have been doing some wishful thinking, nothing more. 'You're probably right,' she admitted slowly, 'but I didn't mean to upset you.'

'I don't get upset,' he refused to be pacified, 'just plain, damn angry!'

'I'm sorry,' she murmured unhappily, staring at his

cold, dark face. 'We can still go to Ascot, though, can't we?'

'No, we can't.'

'Why not?'

Nothing masked the fiery blast of rage in his eyes at her persistence. 'Because I've got other things to do. If you're so desperate to go you must get someone else to take you.'

She knew she wouldn't go without him. She had no fancy to go to Royal Ascot with anyone else or on her own. Half the world would be there. Suddenly she stared at him. What a fool she was! Why did she always forget? Petula would be there; she would rather miss anything than Royal Ascot. Gail remembered her last year in a big, floppy hat, hanging on to Carl's arm, attracting everyone's attention, including that of the media. The newspapers had been loud in their comments on her glamorous image, with several references to her forthcoming marriage to Carl. No wonder he had no wish to appear, this year, with his plain little wife!

'It doesn't matter about Ascot,' she replied haltingly. 'I'm sorry I made such a fuss.'

'Forget it,' Carl muttered briefly, sitting down.

She wished she could forget a lot of things! 'Did you get a good price for Dinkum?' she asked, placing a plate of eggs and bacon before him. 'Gordon Dilston likes a bargain.'

'He got one, in Dinkum, but I didn't let him go for a song.'

He didn't say how much, though. 'I'll be sorry to see him go,' she sighed.

'You're sorry when any of them goes.'

There was no denying it, so she didn't try to. She said slowly, 'Frank and the others will be sorry about Ascot.'

Carl reached for a slice of toast, pushing aside his bacon and eggs. 'We've got another horse running, haven't we?'

'Yes,' she looked at him unhappily, 'but he isn't Dinkum.'

'Not in the same class, I agree.'

There would be little publicity, if he even got a mention! 'He's running in the two-thirty, on Tuesday.'

'So what's the problem, Gail?' He eyed her impatiently again. 'I'm getting rather tired of this conversation. Dick Noble is quite able to manage and the lads will be there to help him. You and I can find other things to do.'

'Such as?'

'Spend the day in bed if you like.'

What doing? Exorcising ghosts? Or was he merely suggesting she could have a rest, on her own? Curious to find out, she adopted his casual tone. 'Who with?'

'Me, perhaps?'

If he had leered at her, she might have thought he was displaying a typically male sense of humour, but he went on eating dry toast as if he wasn't actually conscious of what he was either doing or saying. He wasn't. It didn't take a brilliant intellect to work out that he was thinking of Petula, not of his wife at all.

Gail was so angry, she had to ignore what he said and talk about something else, otherwise she might have exploded! 'I've decided,' she had only just, 'that we should give a small dinner party on Friday night. Will that be all right by you?'

Carl nodded absently and she knew he hadn't heard a word of what she'd been saying, otherwise he would have demanded a guest list and to know how she intended to manage.

Taking advantage of his total withdrawal, she finished her coffee and scrambled to her feet. 'I'm going to put the heating on for Mr Noble. It's June, but the cottage has been empty since we were married.'

'So long?' Carl thrust tense fingers through his black hair as her sudden movement jerked him back to reality. This angered Gail again as he implied that it seemed like a hundred years!

'You heard what I said?' she asked sharply.

'You're going to put the heating on for Dick. Right?'

The hand pushing through his hair came round to explore the roughness of his chin. 'I'm not deaf.'

Sometimes he appeared to be! Hastily she bit her lip, trying to stifle her anger as she noticed how pale he had gone. 'I'll be off, then,' she said unnecessarily.

She had thought he looked so grim he' wouldn't realise she had gone, and was startled when his hand shot out as she went past him, to topple her into his lap.

'How about saying good morning properly,' he demanded huskily, 'before you go? Getting up so early, you obviously forgot.'

Thinking she would never be able to understand him, mutely Gail lifted her soft mouth. His mouth descended gently at first, until a surge of feelings locked them together. She heard a thick noise in his throat as the pressure of his lips deepened. Helplessly her senses began spinning and a kind of drugged heat spread through her body as his arms went tightly round her, folding her close.

Eventually he released her, with some reluctance. 'I could get drunk on kissing you,' he exclaimed tersely. 'God help me, I don't know how it can be!'

'Proximity,' she suggested breathlessly, and wondered, just before she turned and fled from him, why he should suddenly look so remarkably uncertain.

For the next few days there existed a wary harmony between them. Carl slept with her, making love to her with increasing frequency. He wasn't any kinder and his attitude bewildered her, for it sometimes seemed as if he couldn't get enough of her. She couldn't comprehend how he could want her so badly when his feelings weren't involved. Often his approach struck her as being so coldblooded she would stiffen away from him. But his devouring mouth could deal very adequately with such resistance. He could reduce her to lightheaded nothingness in seconds, so she was only capable of clinging to him.

Often during the night, after she had fallen asleep, he would wake her and make love to her again. He would take her almost savagely, knowing he could rely on her instant response. No matter how her mind objected to his silent assault, her body never did. Loving a man, Gail thought bleakly, without being loved in return, didn't do much for one's self-respect. And she was convinced she must be completely without pride where Carl was concerned.

Twice during the week, Carl was away at horse sales. He didn't ask Gail to go with him, but she was so busy planning her dinner party, she didn't mind. She was occupied with other things too. Mary Douglas, Carl's housekeeper, who had left because of his bad temper after he had broken his leg, rang and asked if there was any chance of getting her old job back. Happily—and without consulting Carl—Gail agreed.

Several things flitted through her mind as she arranged to pick Mary up the next day so she could start immediately. In reinstating Mary, she might have acted impulsively, but there were good reasons why they should have some reliable domestic help. The house was too large for her to run satisfactorily alone and she was finding it very difficult to employ anyone locally. The casual help Carl had suggested just didn't seem to be available. He didn't like the idea of someone living in, but he might change his view when he saw the difference it made. And if there was to be no permanency to their marriage, the least she could do was to ensure his home was in good running order before she left.

Strangely enough he raised no objections when she confessed about Mary. 'I suppose a house this size is impossible for a woman to manage single-handed,' he admitted, 'and Mary's not too bad. Did she say what happened to her last employer?'

'He's gone abroad to live with his daughter.'

'And you jumped at the chance when she rang?'

Carl was watching her sardonically, making her defensive. 'Perhaps I was a bit hasty, but it seemed too good a chance to miss. With Mary to help, I'll be able to keep everything in good order, and she'll be very useful when we entertain.'

'Not too much entertaining,' he frowned.

Gail glanced at him uncertainly. He appeared to have forgotten how much he used to enjoy it. 'If we don't do some soon, we might get accused of being unsociable,' she pointed out.

He merely shrugged, as though he wasn't greatly concerned about what people thought. 'Who's coming on Friday?' he asked abruptly.

He hadn't asked before. Taking a deep breath, she reeled off the list of guests. It wasn't very long. There was Ruth and Donald, Sir Arthur and Lady Elliot and a few of their nearest neighbours. 'Grace is in London, so she can't come,' she remembered, explaining about his cousin.

'Good,' Carl said grimly.

Was it for her sake or his own that he was glad Grace wasn't coming? Grace was always loaded with sly remarks which she knew irritated him.

Fortunately Grace remained in London, so nothing threatened the pleasantness of the evening. Twelve guests for a first dinner party might have been ambitious, but with Mary's help Gail coped beautifully. Even Ruth was generous with her praise, while Lady Elliot gave Gail gracious permission to call her Aunt Elizabeth, and allowed her to kiss her cheek as she departed.

Gail grinned when everyone had gone, her sweet young face glowing. 'Your aunt's a darling, but she's so regal she almost frightens me.'

Carl grunted indifferently as he swallowed a last drink, his eyes darkening as they wandered over the provocative curves of her slender figure. Clearly he wasn't thinking of his aunt. 'Come on, let's get to bed,' he drawled. 'If you're capable of walking upstairs, that is?'

Gail's mouth opened indignantly. 'You don't think I'm drunk!'

His brow quirked. 'I mean all the flattery you've been receiving this evening might have gone to your head. I could carry you up. I'm merely taking husbandly precautions.'

Gail laughed, disregarding his offer but throwing him what she suddenly blushed to realise was a flirtatious glance. She did feel lightheaded, but it was because Carl sounded almost proud of her, not because of any flattery she had received from anyone else.

That night, when he made love to her, she seemed to sense a new tenderness in his caresses, but as usual she was so swept away that the next morning she thought she might just have imagined it.

'I want to go to Lambourn, Carl,' she told him at breakfast. 'Mary wants a few things and so do I.'

'Do you want me to take you?' he asked, as Mary bustled in with more toast.

They used the small morning-room now for most of their meals. Carl had said he would as soon carry on having breakfast, anyway, in the kitchen, but Mary had said firmly that she'd rather have the kitchen to herself.

'It's the same wherever you go nowadays,' Carl complained, long-suffering, when Mary left them. 'Servants, if you're lucky—or unlucky—enough to have them, ruling the roost, with the poor man who pays their wages too scared to say a word!'

'What a shame!' Gail giggled. 'Mary's not like that.' And if she had been, she added silently, you would have soon put her in what you consider her place!

'Wives too,' Carl said severely, 'getting above themselves.'

Gail laughed, green eyes dancing. 'Hypocrite!' she jeered. 'I do believe you enjoy it.'

He smiled wryly. 'I'm enjoying seeing you not trying to be in half a dozen places at once, trying to do half a dozen things at the same time. And it's nice to have my wife's undivided attention at mealtimes, not having to compete with the next course.'

'It wasn't as bad as that!' she protested with a giggle.

'My indigestion might disappear too,' he added soberly, 'now that I won't be made to do the washing up.'

'Sometimes you dried the dishes!' she began, then realised he was joking. It was so good to find him in a lighter mood that she held her breath.

His mouth pursed. 'People forget so quickly.'

Gail lowered her thick lashes. He didn't forget Petula quickly. She wished he would. Yet this morning he definitely sounded happier, and she felt a wistful stirring of hope.

'So, do you want anything from town?' She gave a quick glance at the clock. 'If I'm to be back for lunch. You didn't say.'

'No. And you didn't say if you wanted me to take you.'

She shook her blonde head, her eyes warm with appreciation. 'I know you have the vet coming and I haven't a lot of shopping to do. I shan't be long.'

'See you at lunch, then.' Before leaving the room, Carl kissed her briefly. 'Mind you take care.'

Gail had completed most of her purchases when she ran into Grace. If she hadn't been so absorbed, trying to decide the best place to buy the ripe avocados Mary had requested, she might have seen her coming. As it was, Grace stopped right in front of her, so it was impossible to avoid her.

'Oh, hello,' Gail said half-heartedly. 'I thought you were in London?'

'So I was,' Grace shrugged. 'I'm on my way home. I got a lift, but he's gone to spend a penny.'

'Oh, in that case——' Gail tried to edge past her, but Grace caught her arm.

'Wait a minute! I've things to tell you.'

Gail's heart sank.

'Sorry to have missed your do last night,' Grace continued, the smirk on her red mouth not exactly expressing regret. 'I tried to make it, as I had some news for you.'

News from Grace was usually upsetting. 'I'm in a hurry——' Gail backed away.

'Oh, hang on a minute!' Grace implored again, her face full of happy malice. 'You can't be in that great a hurry to return to your—loving husband?'

Why had Grace hesitated on 'loving'? Gail knew an even greater desire to escape. 'Look, Grace, another time, perhaps?'

Grace simply followed as she numbly reversed, and people began to notice and looked amused. Gail was forced to stop. 'Be quick, then,' she said tersely.

'My, my, anyone would think I was your enemy!' Grace commented dryly. 'As your cousin-in-law, I have your interests very much at heart.'

Did she expect to be believed? Gail made no reply, but waited apprehensively.

'So,' Grace went on, her pale eyes lightening with satisfaction, 'can you be surprised that I wanted to make sure you heard the latest news of Petula, before it reached Carl's ears?'

'Petula?'

'Yes.' Coolly Grace studied Gail's suddenly white face. 'Even her name's enough to make strong men blanch, only, in this case, it's a woman.'

Gail maintained a dignified silence. She mightn't be able to prevent Grace seeing she was disturbed, but she wouldn't lose her temper.

'Her marriage isn't going so well,' Grace relayed succulently. 'It's rumoured she's seeking a divorce.'

'Already?'

Grace laughed. 'After a year many people are ready to move on, and in America divorces are two a penny. Even here divorce is becoming a mere formality. An unwanted spouse can be disposed of almost overnight.'

Gail was aware that Grace was hinting at her own marriage, as well as Petula's, and felt a shudder running through her.

'Petula will be at Ascot,' she whispered, almost to herself.

'Uhuh . . .' Grace drawled, beginning to lose interest, now that she had achieved her objective. 'I believe they're coming over.'

'Surely,' Gail heard herself gabbling, 'if she's seeking a divorce, you would think she wouldn't bother, coming here with her husband, I mean?'

'Those kind of people—my kind of people,' Grace taunted, 'take a much broader view of life. We don't have your narrow, provincial little mind. Often couples like Petula and her husband continue associating quite amicably until their divorce comes through. And afterwards.'

Gail turned in distaste, this time determined to escape. 'I really do have to go.'

'Of course!' Grace was all sugary smiles. 'Would you mind, though, passing the information on to Carl? I did promise.'

Promise who? Gail was still trembling as she reached the car. Who could Grace have promised? Hadn't she said she had heard about Petula—nothing about speaking to her! She frowned in utter confusion, not knowing what to think. Grace was fond of twisting things, but she wasn't an out-and-out liar—or was she?

Gail bowed her head over the steering wheel, feeling suddenly sick. She had been beginning to believe her marriage might stand a chance, but now she wasn't so sure. Ugly doubts began presenting themselves again. Desperately she attempted an assessment of Carl's recent attitude towards herself and Deanly. He was more considerate and not quite so scathing in his general remarks, but all too frequently, just when she thought things were getting better, there would be a return of his old harshness.

Gail clenched her hands tightly, trying to think clearly. He was going ahead with his plans to close the training stables, as was proved by the sale of Dinkum, one of their best horses. All of which could be evidence that at least some vague anticipation of Petula's

possible divorce might be lurking at the back of his
mind. Did he intend having all his affairs in order, so he
could easily get away should Petula need him? He
probably had his own divorce half arranged, too, in the
back of his mind.

CHAPTER EIGHT

RETURNING to Deanly, after the sickness which she put down to shock had worn off, Gail decided not to pass Grace's message on to Carl. She might be fighting a losing battle, but she was determined not to give in easily. She refused to hand Carl over on a plate! If Petula wanted him, she must come and get him. And if Grace thought she would actively assist in her own downfall, then she must think again!

Her new bravado, however, wasn't easy to maintain. Her flash of confidence soon disappeared and her spirits sank again to an extremely low level. She was relieved to find, almost as soon as she arrived home, that Carl had arranged for them to attend a race meeting with Dick Noble. He suggested they had a quick bite to eat before leaving.

Gail agreed feverishly, thinking anything was better than having to spend the afternoon alone with Carl and maybe bursting out with some of the things Grace had told her. By the time they returned she might have regained her composure and be more able to keep such things to herself. Besides, with every passing moment she became less inclined to believe Grace had been telling the truth.

Dick Noble wanted to go to this meeting to see a horse run which a friend of his had trained. He had been going on his own, but when his car had broken down, Carl had offered to take him. Gail was getting to know and like the new trainer, something which rather surprised her when she had resented his coming so much. He reminded her of an older version of her father, as he had many of his traits. They passed an enjoyable afternoon, or it would have been enjoyable if she had been able to forget her encounter with Grace!

It was late when they returned to enjoy Mary's delicious dinner. It was sheer luxury to Gail to sit down to a meal someone else had cooked, and she wondered how long it would be before she learned to take such things for granted. She didn't think she ever would— then she remembered she mightn't get the chance, as she might not be here much longer.

Mary popped her head round the dining-room door to say she had left their coffee in the lounge and would they mind if she baby-sat for Jim Stevens and his wife, who wanted to go to a dance in Hungerford.

As Jim Stevens worked on the estate, Carl said it was all right by him, as he knew Jim would see her safely home.

'Shall we watch television?' Gail asked hesitantly, when they went to find their coffee. 'There's a James Bond on.'

Carl opened the window a little, to let in the cool evening air. He seemed restless and sat down with a sigh. 'I shouldn't mind seeing the news,' he replied, 'and I suppose there's no harm in looking at a bit of the film, if the antics of an old James Bond appeals to you?'

Gail nodded, far from enthusiastic herself. She would rather have gone straight to bed as she was tired, but she still hadn't managed to forget her conversation with Grace and knew she wouldn't settle. Half an hour spent watching TV might help her to relax? Not having been able to convince herself that Grace hadn't been telling the truth that morning, she was feeling more depressed than ever. Grace had shattered all her growing optimism regarding the future by filling her with doubts she found impossible to get rid of.

Carl drank coffee and brandy and read during the first half of the film, before switching over for the news. Suddenly Gail gave a small cry of excitement as the news-reader described some trouble in an African state, then announced briefly, 'Here's our man over there, Jeff Lessing, with more details.'

'Carl!' Gail grasped his arm, because he was sitting on the couch beside her. 'Look, it's Jeff!'

'I'm not blind!' he replied coolly, the apprehension in her voice making him frown.

'Oh, shush! Listen!'

'It's you who's making all the noise,' he muttered tersely.

'Sorry.'

They watched as Jeff gave a concise summary of the internal unrest which was causing so much violence and fighting in the country. He was only on for a few minutes but he managed to give a clear picture of what was happening. He looked tired and rather grim.

When his allotted time was up, Gail found a tear on her cheek. Hoping Carl hadn't seen it, she wiped it stealthily away. 'Do you think he's all right?' she asked anxiously.

'Well, he's not exactly in the safest of spots,' Carl said dryly, 'but apart from that, what makes you think he isn't?'

'He seems tired.'

'He probably is.' Carl's tone became even drier, 'I imagine he finds it impossible to get much rest with all that going on, but he's a survivor. I'm sure there's no need to weep over him.'

So he had noticed? She stared blindly at the screen as the newscaster took over again. She should have remembered Carl didn't like her worrying over Jeff. Jeff had a dangerous job, but he could cope. She felt anxious for his safety, but it wasn't the deep fear she would have known had Carl been in danger. But, if she was in danger of losing Carl, it wouldn't be to a horde of enemy guerrillas. It would be to something much more dangerous, she thought with a hollow laugh—another woman!

Like a magnet, her thoughts returned to Petula, her throat tightening frighteningly. Suddenly she knew she had to go to Ascot, to see Petula for herself. Not to speak to, of course, she wouldn't dream of getting that close, but if Petula was there with her husband, surely it would be possible to tell if they were happy together just by looking at them? It might be a crazy thing to do, but wouldn't it be a small price to pay for peace of mind? Her greatest problem might lie in persuading Carl to let her go without him.

When Carl spoke to her again, she turned a face strained by the unhappiness of her thoughts towards him. 'I'm sorry,' she apologised, 'I didn't hear what you were saying.'

'Because you were thinking of someone else,' he retorted grimly, 'another man.'

'Another—man?'

'Don't sound so inncoent,' he said harshly. 'You haven't stopped thinking of Jeff for the past five minutes.' He rose to his feet, switching off the set, twisting the knob viciously, before resuming his seat. 'I'm your husband, remember?'

Did he always remember himself? Apart from taking advantage of the fact to make love to her, what else did to mean to him? She was familiar with his dog-in-the-manger attitude but had no idea of his real feelings.

Suddenly she looked at him defiantly. 'Would you mind if I forgot?'

His eyes narrowed on her face, his gaze cutting and ruthlessly cold. 'Have you?' he countered.

'Answer my question first,' she challenged, with a brittle laugh.

'You don't catch me out that way!' he snarled, catching her by the shoulders, his hands biting into her soft flesh. 'We had an agreement when we got married and I suggest you stick by it without asking questions.'

'There's no harm in talking . . .' Gail protested shakily.

'But no profit in it either. I find this much more satisfying.' Expelling an angry breath, his head swooped towards her, his mouth taking instant possession of her taut lips. She hadn't time to confess that she could never forget him, and that she had been thinking of him, not Jeff.

His fingers wound into a handful of honey-coloured hair, forcing her head still as she would have twisted away. The iron band of his arms crushed her ribs, denying her breath while his mouth brutally smothered the gasping cry of protest which escaped her as she was caught in the dangerous maelstrom of his savage aggression.

Lately he had been different with her, his lovemaking still fiercely passionate but more considerate. Now she had angered him, and when she did he reacted violently. Forcing her mouth open, he plundered it, the quick fury in him tangible through the pressure he exerted. On the shirt she was wearing, buttons snapped as it was swiftly removed to allow his hands direct access to her heated skin. His fingers invaded her bra, pushing up inside it to find the swollen curves of her breasts, his tightening grip betraying increasing impatience.

Dragging his lips from hers, he burned down her throat, his tongue snaking out, as her bra was cast aside, to caress pink peaks until her mind was spinning. She gasped as his hands ran over her fiercely, pressing her hard against him, kissing her ruthlessly.

'Carl,' she pleaded dazedly, 'stop it!'

'Hypocrite!' he bit out. 'Do you really want me to? Your heart's racing.'

Despite the violence of his attack, her hammering heart was responding to the indomitable force of his virility. She trembled at its power.

'Fear!' she gasped.

'My sweet,' he murmured, his narrowed gaze scorching her with mocking fire, 'that's not fear, it's anticipation.'

Oh, how could he humiliate her so! Not content with sending her crazy, he had to sledgehammer her with the truth. And the truth was, as they both knew, that she couldn't resist him, no matter how hard she tried. His breath was hot and disturbing as he whispered his taunts, making her pulses drum frenziedly in her ears. Words of dissent choked in her throat as she couldn't continue denying that she wanted him.

'If you love me,' he muttered harshly, 'why complain?'

'But you don't feel a thing!' she moaned bitterly.

No love for her, she had meant, but Carl apparently misunderstood. 'I feel all right,' he said thickly, his lips moving savagely, burning her already hot flesh, 'I wish I didn't, but with you I can't seem to help myself.'

She was aware of the arousal of his body, for he made no attempt to hide it, but she was hungry for more than that. He pushed her back against the cushions, his length half on her, half beside her, and she tried distractedly to push him away.

'I want a shower,' she cried defensively, trying to ignore the shock waves of sensual pleasure sweeping through her.

Carl's hands were stroking her hips and thighs which he had rendered naked, arousing a conflagration of desire within her as he moulded her to every bruising part of his body. 'We'll have a shower together,' he groaned, in a swift movement throwing off his own clothes, 'but I doubt if right now I could even make the stairs!'

Gail breathed in sharply as his mouth came down on hers again and she was lost. She felt hot with shame as the brush of his naked skin sent her arms tightly round his neck. A primitive, aching need was filling her to the exclusion of everything else, and she despised herself that she could no longer ward off his passionate demands.

'Stop trying to fight me!' Carl gasped hoarsely, sliding between her legs. 'If you do I'll hurt you.'

He did. She felt him shaking and her hands slipped on the sweat that coursed down his shoulders but when she whimpered it was because of the unbearable ecstasy, not pain. She squirmed and surrendered, her hands in his hair, clinging to him frenziedly, moving with him, panting his name. Then he was binding her to him violently as their mouths met and clung and a spiral of growing excitement whipped them fiercely together and the earth fell away. There seemed a kind of glory in the feelings which swept them devastatingly along an irreversible course and on to an even wilder consummation.

Carl was on the phone when she came down on Sunday. Just as she reached him he was saying goodbye to the person he was talking to.

'Good morning,' he said to Gail, as he hung up. His eyes were cool with the familiar wariness in them as she paused beside him.

There was so much she wanted to say, so much that had been left unsaid, last night, as he had commanded her in a hoarse voice not to speak and carried her to bed to make love to her again. The memory of their lovemaking was like a nebulous dream. Come the morning, with Carl's cool, keep-your-distance, eyes on her, she could never believe it was real.

She wanted to talk to him, but the best she could manage was, 'I hope I didn't interrupt . . .'

His mouth quirked suddenly. 'I wouldn't have been cross if you had.'

'Oh,' something in his voice made her eyes widen, 'who was it?'

'Ruth.'

'Ruth?' Startled, Gail searched his face. Ruth never rang this early, unless it was important. 'What did she want?'

'To thank us for the party, for one thing.'

'Oh,' Gail broke in anxiously, 'she was probably trying to get hold of me all day yesterday, while we were out. Didn't Mary say anything? I'd better ring her straight back and apologise.'

'Gail!' he raised a silencing hand, 'your sister was too busy to ring yesterday. She's been apologising.'

'Oh, I see.' Gail flushed, feeling foolish. She was too tense, she knew, and she felt rather odd. 'What else had she to say?'

'We're invited to lunch—for the whole day, if we can stay. I told her we'd be delighted. Was that right?'

'Oh, yes!' Gail was so surprised that Carl had agreed to go, she felt almost overwhelmed. 'Oh, thank you!' she exclaimed, her face suddenly radiant as impulsively she gave him a quick hug.

'Hi!' he caught her arm before she could step away. 'You sound like a little girl who's never been given a treat!'

She looked at him uncertainly, never able to be sure whether he was teasing her or not? 'Don't be silly,' she faltered. 'You're very good to me . . .'

'I try to be.'

She was silent, wondering how she could convince him. He tried to please her, that was the trouble. It didn't come naturally to him, he had to keep reminding himself, making a conscious effort. Continually he must be wrenched between duty, desire and love. The three, intermingled, must make for a perfect marriage, but of the three, the one which would hold a marriage together was love. Desire, a shared mutual passion, might suffice for a while, but in the end, without affection to feed and sustain it, it might easily die. Carl didn't love her, but because they were physically compatible he must be constantly pulled two ways. It was funny, she mused bleakly, how people could become ashamed of wanting but not loving. Eventually Carl would begin to despise himself for wanting her, and waiting for this to happen was getting very hard to bear!

Mary, appearing to tell them breakfast was ready, put an end to further conversation and Carl didn't seem to expect a reply to his brief comment.

'What time shall we set off?' asked Gail, having explained to Mary where they were going and forcing herself to speak brightly as they sat down.

'Twelve-thirty ought to be soon enough,' he muttered absently, obviously losing interest as he picked up the morning paper and began to read.

Ruth welcomed them with a frown. 'Another five

minutes,' she exclaimed, 'and lunch would have been ruined!'

'My fault,' Carl apologised charmingly, coolly kissing Ruth's disapproving mouth. 'I kept Gail waiting.'

He had, it was true, but Ruth didn't have to look that forgiving! Slipping her arm through Carl's, she laughed. 'Let me show you over the house. It seems an appropriate time, now we're leaving.'

Nothing about lunch being on the table, and Ruth as near giggling as Gail had ever seen her. She gasped at the picture of Carl being led off like a lamb, round a huge old vicarage that didn't interest him in the least!

Indignantly she met Donald's twinkling, faintly apologetic glance. 'What's all that about, do you know?'

He said gently, 'Don't mind Ruth, Gail. She's very curious about your marriage and is, I suspect, only trying to get a few things straight in her mind. She doesn't mean any harm.'

Donald smiled reassuringly, but Gail shivered. She was well aware that Ruth had been curious about her marriage since the beginning, but she had no intention of satisfying her curiosity. It wasn't that she resented Ruth being interested in her affairs—after all, she was family—but she would rather die than confess that Carl didn't love her. Ruth was inclined to be outspoken when she thought it necessary. Gail hated to think of the opinion she might express, should she ever discover the truth. That was why Gail was worried about her taking Carl away. Carl wouldn't say anything but Ruth could be remarkably astute. She was good at putting the most unlikely sums together and coming up with the right answer.

Seeing Gail biting her lip, Donald turned her towards the kitchen. 'We always have cold lunch on Sundays so the soup can be the only thing in danger of being ruined. Shall we go and rescue it?'

Gail smiled at him ruefully. 'Perhaps we'd better!'

Ruth said to her while they were washing up, 'Your

husband is charming, Gail. More than charming,' she had a slightly glazed look in her eyes. 'I can understand how women fall for him, all that tallness and sort of prowling darkness. Is it sex appeal?'

'Ruth! You're a vicar's wife!'

'So I am,' Ruth sounded vaguely surprised, 'and rattling away like an impressionable teenager instead of a woman over thirty.'

'Great age,' Gail rejoined mockingly.

Ruth ignored her. 'I don't know, though, how anyone could have walked out on him.'

'No,' said Gail carefully.

'Oh, darling!' Ruth exclaimed in consternation, as Gail managed too late to wipe the fleeting anguish from her face. 'Does he still—I mean . . .'

'No, of course not,' Gail retorted quickly—too quickly, for there was instant suspicion in Ruth's eyes. God, she thought frantically, don't let Ruth suspect anything, I couldn't bear it! It was bad enough as it was, and if Ruth thought something was wrong, what was to stop others thinking the same thing?

'I didn't think he could.' Ruth, with another sharp glance, obviously decided not to probe. 'You're so sweet, I don't see how he could still be in love with another woman.'

Dear Ruth, rough-shodding away.

'Donald was just saying,' Ruth went on blithely, 'how you're turning into a real little beauty. You're developing a dress sense, too, something Petula Hogan didn't have. Well, she spent a fortune on clothes, anyone with half an eye could see that, but something was lacking. I like that dress you have on,' her glance went closely over Gail's blue cotton, which she had thought, with its matching jacket, would be suitable for evening service, if Carl could be persuaded to stay. Ruth's eyes suddenly narrowed. 'You're not as skinny as you used to be. You aren't pregnant, are you?'

'Pregnant? Why—no.' Gail attempted to hide her burning cheeks by bending further over the sink. She couldn't be, could she? It was the last thing Carl would let happen. Or was it?

'I just wondered.' Ruth studied Gail's bowed head thoughtfully. 'You have that look about you.'

'I—have——'

'Oh,' as Gail's hot cheeks paled, Ruth said lightly, 'Take no notice of me. I guess I'm jealous.'

Ruth and Donald couldn't have children, but they were talking about adoption, once they were properly settled in Donald's new parish.

'When do you go?' Gail asked hastily.

'Go? Oh, you mean move?' Ruth smiled happily, allowing herself to be diverted. 'The removal people are coming on Wednesday. There's been so much to do, it's been rather hectic.'

Gail felt immediately guilty. 'I could have helped. I didn't think, but if you'd given me a ring . . .?'

Ruth smiled and shook her head. 'If I'd needed you I wouldn't have hesitated, but the removal men appear to like doing most of the actual packing themselves. And we haven't a lot of stuff. One thing about moving every few years, you don't get a chance to accumulate.'

'Is your next vicarage just as big?'

'Larger,' Ruth shrugged. 'These places tend to swallow one up, but somehow, if the cost of heating and cleaning wasn't so high, I prefer them to the smaller houses the powers that be are replacing them with today.'

When Carl and Gail left, Ruth whispered, 'Mind, you tell me if—well, you know what I said!'

'What was all that about?' Carl asked idly, as they drove away.

Gail turned and waved again, despite the fact that the Vicarage was out of sight. 'Just asking me to keep in touch.'

'Rather an unsual way of putting it!'

Gail flushed. 'Ruth's like that.'

'I never realised she could be so charming,' he said reflectively.

She glanced at him sharply. 'Ruth said the same thing about you.'

'Ah,' he grinned, and Gail could imagine him and Ruth, skirting round each other like a couple of predators, each warily cautious of the other, giving nothing away.

'Did you enjoy your tour of the house?' she asked coolly.

'Yes,' he said. 'Your sister's very knowledgeable about antiques.'

Was that all they had discussed or was he just being discreet? Gail sighed and said, 'I hope they'll be happy in their new home.'

'I'm sure Ruth will take it in her stride,' he said smoothly. 'After they get settled in you'll have to go for a weekend.'

You'll have to—not, we'll have to. It might only have been a slip of the tongue, but she dared not ask for fear it wasn't? 'Donald might be there for several years,' she replied evasively. 'It's a much bigger parish with more responsibilities.'

'Poor man, he'll be run off his feet.'

'Probably, but he likes it that way.'

'Nice chap, your brother-in-law.'

Donald was, and she might have appreciated Carl's comment if he hadn't been in the habit of talking of Ruth and Donald so vaguely, almost as though they had nothing to do with him. That was the trouble, she realised apprehensively, he didn't think they had, not permanently. His thoughts were wholly on the future, a future in which neither she nor her family had any place!

The following day, after lunch, when she felt she couldn't leave it any longer, she asked Carl if she could go to Ascot. She waited until he had finished eating, so if he was angry and stalked out, he wouldn't be deprived of his meal.

He put down his coffee cup with a discouragingly sharp bang as he fixed her with a cold gaze. 'I thought we'd been through all that, and it was all settled?'

She gazed back at him, a tiny pucker on her smooth forehead. With Carl one had to be so careful. If she showed too much enthusiasm he would immediately become suspicious. If she was too casual about it, he would assume it didn't matter and refuse to even consider letting her go.

'I think one of us should be there to see our horse run.'

Carl's eyes didn't waver. 'I'd have thought Dick and Frank should be enough. It's just one race.'

Unhappily she glanced away from him. 'I would like to go.'

'And that's really the crux of the matter, isn't it?' he said curtly. 'You like the excitement of a big race meeting? Seeing Kerry run is merely incidental.'

Gail didn't argue. It might be wiser to let him think that, if she was to stand a chance of getting his consent. There was just a chance that he might believe it better to wean her gradually. 'It would just be for one day.'

To her surprise, she must have been fairly accurate in her conclusions, for he didn't get angry. He had been about to get up, but instead he stayed where he was, looking at her thoughtfully.

'You'd have to go with Dick and you'd have a lot of people asking where I was. It could be embarrassing.'

He was frowning, as if he suddenly didn't like the picture of her being alone and unprotected, exposed to the cynically barbed wit of some of his acquaintances. Gail's heart warmed to him, even as she wondered nervously what he would say if he knew the real reason why she felt so compelled to go to Ascot.

'I'll come to no harm,' she assured him quickly. 'I'll stay with Dick and the boys and probably no one will notice me. Anyway, I know the course so well, I could never get lost.'

'You'd better not!' Carl retorted so threateningly, that she might have thought he cared, if she hadn't known differently.

She drove to Ascot with Frank and Dick Noble. All
the way the talk was of horses, but for once Gail was
content to listen, having so much else on her mind. The
roads were crowded, but Dick, an old hand at the
game, achieved the impossible by getting them to the
course on time.

Frank was doubtful regarding the weather. 'If it
doesn't stop raining, the horses will be finishing down
under. Australia,' he quipped, with a quick glance at
Gail to make sure she understood.

Hoping she wasn't as dense as all that, Gail nodded
with due appreciation while Dick's iron grey brows
quirked dryly as he concentrated on getting parked.

For Gail, though the actual racing wasn't so
important any more, she didn't think anyone could fail
to be impressed by the sheer magic of a big race
meeting, particularly Ascot. The Royal Family alone,
as they drove to the course each day in open landaus,
was a sight never to be forgotten. Thousands of
visitors from all over the world flocked to the famous
Berkshire course, so near Windsor, the Queen's country
home, and the sophisticated fashions of beautiful
women accompanied by men smartly attired in
morning dress, made it a particularly glamorous
occasion. In Gail's estimation, although it now took
second place in her life, there was nothing quite like
the excitement of it all. She loved the crowds, their
noisy exuberance, their thunderous roars of encouragement and deprecation during the actual
racing, the groans and the cheers at the end. She had
shared so much in the heartache and triumph, she felt
somehow it was part of her. Yet she knew if it hadn't
been for Petula, she would much rather have been at
Deanly with Carl.

The course was packed, the crowds goodnatured,
their spirits rising as the clouds cleared and the sun
came out, but without Carl something was missing.
Without him Gail felt oddly alone. She went with Dick
and Frank to ensure their horse had arrived safely and

that their jockey was there, then she left them to wander on her own.

Dick Noble frowned worriedly when she said she would see him later. 'Your husband told me not to let you out of my sight,' he explained, 'so I think you should stay with me.'

'I saw some old friends,' she improvised hastily. 'After I have a chat with them I'll come back.'

'Who are they?' Dick asked awkwardly.

'The Greenlaws,' quickly she thought of some neighbours who never missed Ascot. 'And I might try and find the Purdies, my father used to train for them.'

Dick seemed moderately satisfied that she would be all right, but he insisted that she returned at a certain time. 'I know you must think I'm stepping out of line and that what you do is none of my business,' he apologised anxiously, 'But above all, I'm answerable to your husband. And he didn't exactly mince his words!'

Gail didn't think Carl would, though she couldn't understand why he should be making such a fuss. She felt like telling Dick that she wasn't a child but a grown woman, quite capable of looking after herself and making her own decisions, but somehow she couldn't. He looked so uncomfortable that she found herself promising to return in time to see their horse run.

Which didn't give her all that much time to accomplish what she had come to do. Not only had she to find Petula, she had to try and discover whether she was still a contented wife, or on the verge of a divorce, as Grace had sworn she was. And she had to find her first!

It wasn't easy, especially as so many people spotted her and stopped to talk. It seemed like a retaliatory blow from fate, when she had had no intention of looking for the Purdies, that they saw her and Lady Purdie pounced, with all the determination she was capable of. There was no way of avoiding her. Gail knew Lady Purdie was aware of her marriage, as Ruth had met her in town and they had had lunch together, but this was the first time Gail had seen her this year.

'You naughty child!' Lady Purdie exclaimed. 'Getting married, and to Carl Elliot, without sending me an invitation!'

'It was a very quiet wedding,' Gail began.

'And who had more right to be there than I?' Lady Purdie drew herself up majestically, everything about her wobbling. 'Didn't I practically rear you? Dear Ruth has always appreciated me!'

Lady Purdie talked that way, like she made a habit of rearing stray chickens. She meant no harm, Gail tried to assure her rising irritation.

'Perhaps you and Lord Purdie would care to call one day?' She knew better than to suggest a date herself. 'Carl would be delighted to show Lord Purdie round. You could give us a ring when it's convenient.'

Lady Purdie appeared faintly mollified, as Gail edged away. 'Thank you, my dear. I'll certainly be in touch. I have a wedding present.'

That must be the crowning mark of approval! Gail thought wryly, struggling on through the crowds. Lady Purdie never bestowed her favours lightly. When her niece had married a farm worker, she hadn't given them a thing.

Meeting so many people, Gail was glad Carl had insisted she wore a dress, but when her hat was constantly either knocked or falling off, she grew increasingly agitated as she was sure that having continually to rescue it must have caused her to miss Petula. When she saw her, at last, Petula was making her way towards the Royal Enclosure. She was with two other couples and a tall, florid-looking man, who Gail presumed was her husband. Almost holding her breath, she studied them closely, as they paused to speak to another group of people.

Petula, as usual, was attracting attention, but when she wasn't deliberately smiling at one of the many sniping photographers, her heavily made up face wore a discontented expression. The man by her side didn't look any happier either. In fact, he and Petula were acting like a couple of strangers. None of which, Gail realised, with a surge of self-impatience, proved their marriage was breaking up!

Suddenly she knew she had been extremely foolish in coming here today. Clenching her hands tightly, she felt suddenly desperately ashamed of herself. Just what had she hoped to achieve? What could she possibly have achieved? Lots of people quarrelled. If Petula and her husband didn't appear to be speaking to each other, it might prove no more than that they'd had a temporary disagreement.

Swallowing unhappily, she was just about to turn and run, when to her horror Petula glanced around and their eyes met. Gail saw the other woman's eyes widen, then narrow, but as she began walking towards her, Gail fled.

Furious with herself for being so careless, Gail began stumbling and scrambling back the way she had come, all the time berating her own foolishness. In coming here today, she had allowed her love for Carl and her sense of insecurity to drive her beyond the bounds of what could ever be described as sensible, but she ought to have made sure Petula didn't see her. Now that Petula had, Gail tried to convince herself it couldn't matter, but she had a horrible feeling she was wrong!

She was panting when she reached the stables, only to find that the men from Deanly had gone. They would be in the parade ring. She was on her way to find them when, retracing her steps round a quiet corner, she almost bumped into Petula.

While she was still gasping, Petula said sharply, 'Why didn't you wait when I called? You must have known I want to speak to you!'

No form of greetings. Just a snapping and snarling which made Gail feel apprehensively that she was being attacked! Petula looked so livid that Gail quailed, and her heart began hammering so hard she felt ill. 'I had no idea,' she murmured feebly. Then, with a little more courage, 'Why should you want to speak to me?'

Icily, Petula retorted, 'Perhaps I wanted to congratulate you on being so clever, for catching Carl on the rebound!'

Gail gulped, then stiffened. Petula might believe in laying her cards on the table, but she didn't have to put up with anyone's insults! 'I'd get your facts right, if I were you,' she suggested coldly, taking a deep breath to try and steady her racing pulse. 'Carl isn't the kind of man who'd do anything unless he wanted to, and we're very happy.'

'You mean you are?'

As she could never remember Petula speaking to her pleasantly, Gail wasn't surprised at her vicious tone. She wasn't surprised, either, that Petula was apparently furious that Carl had married someone else as she was a woman who liked to think a man remained her property even when she had no further use for him. She had always been extremely possessive. At Deanly, Gail recalled, whenever anyone had gained Carl's attention, Petula had always quickly dragged him away.

'Carl's very happy too,' she reiterated determinedly, her face nevertheless paling before the other girl's vindictive stare.

CHAPTER NINE

'I DON'T believe you,' Petula said sharply.

Gail stared at her defiantly. 'I don't care whether you do or not.'

'You might when you hear I'm getting a divorce,' Petula retorted furiously. 'And you don't have to pretend to be surprised. Grace, Carl's cousin, mentioned it to you. I've just been speaking to her.'

'She—she said something,' Gail stammered vaguely,

'Did you tell Carl? He'd be interested.'

'No, I didn't.' Gail felt suddenly furious. 'Why should I? It's probably not the only divorce you'll have, so why should he be interested?'

'Why indeed?' Petula drawled, Gail's angry words bouncing off her supreme self-confidence. 'I'll be free any day now and you'll soon see if he's interested or not! When I do that!' she clicked insolent fingers in Gail's stunned face, 'he'll have left you before you realise what's happening.'

'No, he won't!' Gail whispered hoarsely, wondering why she sounded like she was uttering a prayer.

'You'd better make sure he gets the message this time,' Petula snapped, 'or I shouldn't like to be in your shoes.'

'Tell him yourself!' said Gail, between clenched teeth.

'I would have done, had he been here,' Petula replied smugly. 'Of course, I'm not surprised that he isn't. Not when he must be remembering last year.'

Gail felt she was being backed into a corner, fighting desperately for her life. 'That doesn't mean a thing. He married me, which proves he has forgotten.'

'For how long?' Petula crowed, her near-black eyes glittering triumphantly.

Gail shuddered. Petula might be beautiful, and

149

beautifully attired, in a bold black and white dress with a pintucked front which hid her lack of shape, and a huge floppy hat, but somehow she reminded Gail of a raucous crow.

A penetrating announcement over a loudspeaker released her numbed limbs. Quickly she turned from Petula, without answering her last question or attempting to say goodbye.

'Don't forget what I've told you!' Petula called threateningly after her, but Gail gave no indication of having heard her.

When she returned to Deanly, Carl was out. An hour later, when he came in, he said he had been to Lambourn and been held up. Apart from enquiring if she'd had a good day, he asked few other questions. For once, Gail didn't regret his lack of interest. In fact, she would have liked it better if he'd asked no questions at all. If he had completely ignored her trip to Ascot, she felt she might have had a more concrete excuse for not mentioning she had seen Petula. She talked of her meeting with the Purdies, how Lady Purdie was about to honour them with a visit, then a lot about the way his horse had run, more than she might otherwise have done if her conscience hadn't been bothering her.

Thinking her marriage might soon be ruined by deception rather than saved by it, she went upstairs to have a shower before going to bed. Carl had retreated to his study, cutting abruptly through her bright but over-long monologue as to why Kerry had only come in fourth. She wasn't surprised when he didn't follow. If he slept at all that night it wasn't with her. Unhappily Gail cried herself to sleep. It was very obvious that because Carl must have guessed Petula was in the country, he couldn't face sleeping with the woman who, unfortunately, was his wife!

The following day, although Ruth had told her it wasn't necessary, she went to see if she could assist. There was, Gail soon discovered, quite a lot she was able to do, and it warmed her aching heart slightly when Ruth assured her, as she waved them off, that if it hadn't been for her help, neither she nor Donald might have been able to leave before the next morning.

Carl was coming from the study as she got in. 'I've just had your friend Ann Morris on the phone,' he said. 'She was on about the gymkhana at Headlands next week. It seems she's been trying to get in touch.'

Gail frowned. The Morrises were Carl's friends as well as hers, he had known them longer. 'Didn't you explain that I've been busy?'

'I tried,' he shrugged. 'I told her about your sister moving and whatnot, but she seems to think it no excuse for forgetting something that's held every year.'

A flicker of uncertainty flashed across Gail's face. She hadn't been feeling so good lately, she didn't seem to have half the energy she usually had. She could never remember being so easily tired.

'Are you going to help?' she asked tentatively. 'You usually do.'

'I have done occasionally,' he corrected coolly.

Uneasily she asked him outright. 'Will you be going?'

He swung on her sharply, his fingers raking irritably through his thick dark hair. 'What is this, Gail? First Ascot, now the bloody gymkhana. Are you afraid to let me out of your sight?'

Horrified, she gazed at him, half frozen by nameless fears. The buttons of his shirt were undone, revealing the mat of crisp hair on his chest, while under the shirt muscles rippled. His virile masculinity seemed to wrap round her with suffocating intensity, making her tremble. But his manner made her tremble even more. He had never spoken to her quite like this before.

'Why should I be afraid to let you out of sight?' she mumbled, praying he didn't suspect anything.

'I don't know.' Suddenly he seemed to back down slightly, as if getting himself under control. 'Maybe you still worry about me?'

'Worry about you . . .?'

'My leg. It's better now, so you don't need to.'

Why did she feel he was prevaricating? 'I don't worry about your leg,' she replied tensely. 'You don't exactly invite sympathy. As for not going anywhere without you,' she persisted, when he would obviously rather have dropped the subject, 'surely you can't feel resentful because I assumed you'd be going to Ascot and the gymkhana, events you always go to?'

'I don't always go anywhere!'

She felt like hitting him. He was twisting her words because he was in a bad mood! Anger flared through her. 'You've stopped going to some places because you're afraid!'

'Afraid?'

Her eyes challenged him to deny it. If he had been trying to provoke her he had succeeded. Too late she regretted allowing herself to retaliate so impulsively. 'Carl,' she pleaded suddenly, 'let's not quarrel.'

'Why am I afraid to go to places?' he asked, his voice silky with menace.

She had appealed to him too late, she realised helplessly. They were set on a collision course and she'd be wasting her time trying to avoid the final outcome. 'You know why,' she sighed wearily. 'You're afraid of meeting Petula.'

His hand shot out, contacting her cheek, in a stinging slap. As she reeled back, he snapped, 'You aren't fit to mention her name!'

She flinched without replying, merely standing looking at him, a red mark on her cheek where he had struck her, her eyes a wounded, haunting green. He had hurt her, but at least he had answered the question which had tormented her near to total misery. Their marriage had no chance of succeeding, a fact which she must now accept.

With hands clenched tightly by her sides, she turned from him.

'Where are you going?' he rasped.

'Upstairs,' she spoke like a zombie. 'Maybe out—I'm not sure.'

'As long as you understand the situation?'

She nodded dully but didn't look at him, so he wouldn't see her tears.

'Good.' His voice followed her trailing figure as she moved away from him. 'Don't forget to get in touch with Ann and confirm that you're willing to help next week.'

Gail was glad of the gymkhana, for the work it entailed kept her occupied and away from Deanly for hours at a time. Ann Morris proved a real friend. She was older than Gail, and though Gail didn't take her into her confidence, she seemed to sense something was wrong between her and Carl, and Gail felt comforted by her unspoken sympathy. Some might have resented it, she knew, but, these days, she seemed to have little pride left. Besides, Ann was such a nice, warm person, and she didn't pry.

Ann and her husband, Chris, who was nice too, rented one of the medium-sized farms in the area, and although they neither bred or trained horses, they liked to keep a few. Mostly they were old horses, pensioned off, horses they were too fond of to part with, but they usually managed to have at least two well able to compete in the numerous local events which took place all over the county during the summer months.

The gymkhana was arranged for the twenty-seventh of June and, that morning, Carl told Gail he had to go to London.

'I'll probably be gone the whole weekend,' he said curtly.

Gail gazed at him uncertainly. She had been so busy lately, helping Ann and the committee with the programme and getting her own horse ready, that she had seen little of him. She was aware that she had been deliberately keeping out of his way, but she still found the memory of their last conversation too painful to risk being hurt again. The final hurt, she realised, would come soon enough, and she prayed, when it did, she would find the courage to cope with it.

Carl hadn't been to her room since Ascot and she saw a change in him. He was pale beneath the tan he always had from being so much out of doors and his eyes looked strained. 'London?' she echoed woodenly.

'Yes.' His mouth tightened grimly while her smarting green eyes fell to study his sleeve. 'Do you mind?'

She shrank from his tone while reminding herself she should be used to it. 'No, of course not.'

'I hope the weather stays fine for you,' he remarked stiltedly, and departed.

As soon as he had gone, Gail left for Headlands. It was far too early, but there was still plenty to do and she couldn't bear to stay at home, having Mary fussing over her, as she had been doing recently, telling her she didn't look well. She knew what Mary was thinking, it was no more than she was thinking herself, but she preferred to keep her suspicions to herself. Besides, she would need an excuse for going to see a doctor, if Carl wasn't to suspect anything, and right now, she didn't have an excuse.

Because she had been feeling ill and suspected the cause, she had only agreed to compete in one race. A fairly easy one, involving just a few hurdles. It was because she couldn't seem to concentrate on what she was doing that her horse stumbled and fell at the last jump. She was both startled and disgusted to find herself lying on the ground, because the course had been one she could normally have completed without mishap in her sleep.

'Don't ask me how I managed it,' she groaned derisively, as Ann and Chris hurried to her assistance. 'Serves me right for becoming too complacent, I suppose!'

'Never mind that,' Chris exclaimed, too concerned to share her attempted joke. 'Are you all right? You've got a bump on your head, love.'

'It's nothing,' she grasped his arm as he helped her up and she felt dizzy.

Ann, scrutinising Gail's shocked face closely, said briskly. 'It's the doctor for you, my child.'

'No!' Gail protested quickly. 'I'll be fine in a minute.'

'Where the hell is Carl?' she heard Chris mutter in a swift aside to his wife, as she bent her head quickly to prevent herself from fainting.

She sensed rather than saw the imperceptible shake of Ann's head and repeated again, 'I'm quite all right.' She didn't feel it. She was actually feeling rather dreadful and guessed she looked it. Hence Chris's alarm.

'I think we should ring for the doctor,' Ann insisted.

'No!' Gail's voice rose hysterically. 'You don't call a doctor out just for a little toss from a horse.'

'Tell you what,' Ann suggested lightly, with another cautioning glance at her worried husband, 'I'll drive you to the clinic. As it's Saturday there won't be a surgery proper, but there's always someone on duty.'

Gail was about to make a further protest when she realised suddenly that it might be a good idea. At least she had a good excuse for discovering if there was anything wrong with her, without anyone being any the wiser.

In a very short time they arrived at the clinic, run by a panel of doctors. The one Gail saw was one whom she had become familiar with through the stables, where occasionally, small incidents occurred. Gail, with her excellent health, rarely needed to consult a doctor, but Doctor Harding had been very kind when her father died.

It amazed her how medical people could often seem to diagnose one's condition at a glance. After assuring her that he didn't think the bump on her head would produce any serious repercussions, he asked her carefully how she was feeling otherwise.

When Gail flushed and found herself confessing to other symptoms which had nothing to do with her fall, he nodded and very quickly confirmed that she was pregnant. She was fit and well, he said, if a little on the thin side. He advised her to rest over the weekend and not to go riding again until he made sure she was fully recovered from this afternoon's mishap.

'It's just a precaution, Gail,' he smiled, 'but at this stage it's never wise to take risks. I'm sure your husband's going to be delighted.'

That might be the last thing Carl would be, Gail thought unhappily, as she left the surgery and tried to smile brightly at her waiting friend.

'What did he say?' asked Ann anxiously.

'Nothing much,' Gail replied lightly. 'There's no real damage. He's given me some tablets in case my head aches and said to take things easy over the weekend.'

As they got back into the car, Ann continued looking at her keenly. 'And the other?'

'Wh-what other?' Gail stammered, clenching her hands. Oh, God, was it that obvious?

'You—know,' Ann said gently.

Her gentleness was Gail's undoing. 'I——' she began, then suddenly capitulated as she was forced to swallow a sob. 'How did you guess?'

'Instinct, feminine,' Ann muttered briefly, then enquired abruptly, as she realised Gail was upset, 'Doesn't Carl know yet?'

'Carl? Oh, no ...!' Gail's face went oddly paler. 'Please don't tell him! I mean,' she amended in confusion, 'promise you won't say anything until I've had time to.'

'I promise,' Ann assured her with a wry grin. 'I'm not stupid. I won't mention it to a soul, not even Chris. You can rely on me.'

She dropped Gail off at Deanly after arranging for the return of Gail's horse. 'I'm sure Frank or some of your lads will have seen to it, but if not, Chris and I will bring him back and pop him in his box. We won't disturb you but I'll give you a ring tomorrow, just to see how you're getting on. Carl might be home by then?'

Mary met her at the door. She hadn't gone to the gymkhana as she'd been to both a fête and a garden party during the past few days, and, to use her own words, thought she'd done enough gallivanting for one week! Frank had been in touch, though, telling her what had happened, and she was worried.

'Oh, my goodness, Gail!' She still called Gail, at Gail's insistence, by her Christian name unless someone else was present. 'What a fright you've given me, child! I told that stupid Frank, Mr Elliot'll murder him, when he gets back, letting something happen to you.'

Gail doubted it, while she hushed her weakly. 'It wasn't Frank's fault, Mary, and it was only a tiny spill.'

'That's as may be!' Mary sniffed. 'But he ought to have been keeping a closer eye on you. You've been to the doctor's?'

She must have learnt that from Frank too. As Gail nodded and Mary ushered her carefully inside, like Ann, she wanted to know what the doctor had said.

Taking a deep breath, Gail replied, 'He advised me to take things easy for the weekend, but I'm quite all right.'

She wanted to go to the kitchen and sit down, but Mary insisted she went straight to bed.

'Shouldn't I send for Mr Elliot?' she asked, glancing as doubtfully as Ann had at Gail's pale face.

'Oh, no!' Panic brought the first tinge of colour to Gail's white cheeks. 'He mustn't be bothered. He has important business.'

Mary didn't appear to disbelieve her, but she frowned. 'What could be more important than his wife?'

Just about everything, flashed through Gail's mind bitterly. Aloud, she said, 'I think I will go to bed. I feel a bit funny.'

Upstairs, she was sick. Mary didn't say anything, but waited until she felt better then helped her to wash and get into her pyjamas. She tucked her in with gentle hands before leaving her to make a cup of tea. 'Don't move until I get it,' she said firmly.

Dear Mary! Gail felt a lump come to her throat. Mary had been at Deanly about a year longer than she had, and had always made a fuss of her. She had missed her pleasant, motherly presence after she had gone and felt happier each day at having her back.

Mary sat with her while she drank her tea, which surprisingly settled her tummy. Mary also brought her a dry cracker biscuit and watched with knowledgeable eyes as she ate it. 'That usually does the trick,' she commented mysteriously.

Gail didn't ask her to be more specific, she was too busy thinking of Carl. 'He might be here tomorrow,' she whispered, half to herself.

'Mr Carl? I hope he is!' Mary said tartly. 'He should be here with you now.'

Sensing unspoken criticism, Gail bristled, 'Sometimes he has to be away!'

Mary, realising she was doing nothing to soothe her patient, apologised. 'I'm sorry, child. You're right, of course.'

Gail blinked eyes blinded with sudden tears. 'I miss him so much, Mary,' she confessed pathetically.

'I know, dear,' Mary swallowed what seemed suspiciously like a lump in her throat, 'I know how much you think of him.'

'I love him,' Gail said simply.

'He's a lucky man.' Mary's tone implied that she hoped he realised it. 'Do you know, dear, when he didn't marry that other one, I really did thank the good Lord. I know I left him when I shouldn't, but my nerves got so bad through trying continually to convince him, without putting it in words, if you understand, how he'd had a lucky escape. He resented it, naturally, and got so bad to put up with, I just had to have a break. I always knew I'd come back, though. And when I heard he'd married you, I was so pleased it was a pleasure to come back. I just hope he appreciates his good luck, that's all.'

In a way, once she began feeling better, Gail was almost as relieved as sorry that Carl wasn't at home that weekend. His absence gave her a chance to decide whether or not to tell him about the baby. He'd been so unsettled lately, she was terrified that he might believe she had got pregnant deliberately in an attempt to keep him tied to a marriage he didn't really want. She wished she knew where he was, what he was doing and thinking. She was haunted by the thought that he might be with Petula, although Petula would surely be back in America by now.

Gail sighed. The truth was, no matter how she tried to avoid it, that Carl resented being married to her, and with a baby on the way he could feel doubly trapped. Not all men fantasised over a son and heir! If he decided definitely that they must part, it might be better if he didn't know about the baby.

Yet, Gail pondered, mightn't there be another way of looking at things? Their marriage hadn't been a complete failure. Physically they were very compatible, and if she was sometimes ashamed of her own wantonness in Carl's arms, she knew her complete inability to prevent herself from responding to him pleased him greatly. And, as she frequently told herself, they shared a close affinity in other ways as well, a love of Deanly and horses and the countryside being not the least among them. Suddenly she decided, when he returned, she would gamble on the strength of what they had and tell him about the baby. It might be a foolish thing to do, risking everything in one final throw, so to speak, but it might make Carl realise he had something much more worthwhile to live for than Petula. When Gail thought of the child she was carrying, perhaps a small replica of Carl, with other children to follow, it made her heart swell with a wonderful kind of joy. Surely, she thought, with a surge of new optimism, if she felt like this, Carl couldn't help but share her feelings?

Carl didn't return home on Sunday, as she had secretly hoped he might, nor did he ring. On Monday, fearing she might go slightly mad if she stayed in the house, listening for his car or the phone any longer, she went with Dick Noble in the Land Rover to watch one of the afternoon gallops. There was a horse Dick was particularly interested in, and for a while Gail was able to put some of her worries aside as she shared in his enthusiasm.

It was four when she got back to the house, and to her delight, Carl's car was in the drive. Mary was nowhere to be seen and when she couldn't find Carl, either, Gail assumed he must be upstairs. Forgetting how stormily they had parted, she ran eagerly to find him.

At their bedroom door, she paused a moment to get her breath back before opening it, but when she did she stopped, aghast. Carl was standing beside some of the lightweight luggage he used when he was flying. He had obviously been packing to go abroad. Her bewildered eyes rose slowly to his face. His hair had a dampness which betrayed that he had recently showered, but he was tightening his tie as if he had immediately dressed again. She began to tremble like a leaf, wondering where he was going, feeling suddenly lost and afraid.

Instinctively she tried to be calm. She hadn't seen what he had put in his car before he'd gone to London. Maybe the luggage she was looking at was just what he had brought back, although he didn't usually pack two cases for a single weekend.

'Hello,' she said nervously, feeling her way.

When he didn't reply, she knew an immediate sense of desolation. It began beating through her, drowning all her newly-found hopes for the future. It was the end, she knew it as clearly as if Carl had just spelt it out, and there was not a thing she could do about it. It was like kneeling at the executioner's block with her hands tied behind her back. It might be futile, she realised, to utter even one word in protest. The expression on Carl's face was that of a man whose mind was already made up. Not only that, it came to her like a terrible shaft of fear, he had obviously things to say which were going to make for far from pleasant hearing.

'What are you doing?' she asked huskily, as he still didn't speak.

'That should be perfectly obvious,' sarcastically his eyes fell to the cases at his feet. 'I'm leaving.'

No preliminary announcement, nothing to soften a blow which he must know was excruciating.

'Leaving?' she gasped, for all she had known it, her face as white as a sheet.

'I wish,' he rasped icily, 'you wouldn't keep repeating everything after me, like a child at school!'

That didn't tell her exactly what she was trying to discover. Futilely she refused to give up hope completely. 'Will you only be away a few days again?'

'No,' he said harshly, 'I'm going for good. Out of your life for good, that is. One day I'll be coming back to live here, but it won't be with you.'

'Carl!' Her feet stumbled towards him, her hands clutching his arm. Frantically she cried, 'You can't mean that!'

Without pity he looked down into her anguished eyes. 'I'm afraid I do.'

'But—why?'

Roughly he shook her off, his jaw set hard. 'How about answering some of my questions for a change? You didn't tell me you'd seen Petula at Ascot!'

So that was it! Gail folded her arms across her heaving breast, gazing at him in bleak despair. 'What would have been the point? She hurt you before. I didn't want it to happen again. I was trying to protect you.'

'People hurt each other all the time,' he snapped indifferently. 'She realises she hurt me, but she was confused. When she was engaged to me, her feelings had never been so involved before, and she suddenly became frightened.'

'So frightened she married another man!' Gail mocked sharply.

Carl's eyes glinted with increased anger as he sensed her scorn. Gail realised, with a shiver of shock, that he was struggling not to hit her. 'She felt safe with Oscar,' his voice softened slightly. 'He was like a harbour in a storm. It wasn't until she married him that she realised what she'd given up.'

She went on staring at him. Could that be true? Loving Carl, she had to admit she was sometimes frightened by the strength of her own emotions. Yet though perhaps people reacted differently, she knew she could never have left him and married another man. If Carl went away, there would never be anyone else for her. Despite this, she would be willing to let him go, if she could have believed Petula really loved him and would have made him happy.

'It's possible she left you for—for the reasons she's given,' Gail allowed reluctantly, 'but doesn't she have any conscience about leaving her husband?'

'It's not a case of conscience,' Carl retorted curtly. 'She couldn't make him happy when she can think only of me.'

Gail looked at him incredulously. Did he really believe it? Her heart sank as something in his eyes convinced her he did. 'And you?' she whispered unevenly.

He said tersely, 'Sometimes one has to be cruel to be kind. Once you're free, you'll be able to find another man who can give you everything I can't.'

'You mean you intend divorcing me?'

'I intend seeing my solicitor in the morning, before I leave for New York.'

Everything went black. Gail swayed, but the room slowly righted itself. 'You—you won't change your mind?'

'No,' he said roughly, anger hardening his eyes again. 'What else did you expect, Gail? You've deceived me all along.'

'Deceived you?'

'I saw Petula in London this weekend,' he said grimly.

Gail's face went so stiff she could scarcely speak. 'You're already—together?'

'No!' he glared at her in tight-lipped fury, 'we are not already together! I haven't touched her—if that satisfies your nasty little mind! She rang on Friday, to tell me her divorce was through. She was surprised that I knew nothing about it. It appears you failed to deliver her message—the one she gave you at Ascot.'

Gail said, her voice shaking. 'Would you have passed on such a message, from another man, if our positions had been reversed? For instance,' she thought distractedly, 'if it had been from Jeff?'

His eyes sharpened. 'Don't be a fool,' he said crushingly. 'Leave Jeff out of this.'

Suddenly she felt too weary to say she had merely been using Jeff as an example. 'Hasn't our marriage meant anything to you?' she implored miserably.

'Oh, for God's sake!' he snapped angrily. 'You knew when you married me that there was little chance of our relationship being permanent. It wasn't a normal marriage.'

'You—you made it one.'

Carl stared at her, his body rigid, rage fighting with something she couldn't decipher in his dark face. 'You didn't exactly discourage me,' he retorted cruelly. 'Proximity had a lot to do with it. I believe you sensed I was fighting it, yet you couldn't stay out of my bed.'

Her face suffused with colour. 'I . . .'

He cut her off ruthlessly. 'Why bother to deny it? You were ready to melt in my arms every time I got near you. I'm a man, Gail, with a normal sexual appetite, and as a woman, even a fairly innocent one, you couldn't help taking advantage. I know I'm stronger than you, but it's not always easy to resist something that's handed to you on a plate.'

She felt so dreadful, she wished she could have sunk through the floor. Her mouth trembled from trying to form words which wouldn't come.

'You can't say I deceived you,' he added.

No, she could never say that. Her taut lips moved at last. The remorseless things Carl was saying tore her apart and she wondered why she persevered. 'I thought you'd come to care for me a little?'

'It's possible,' he allowed, his eyes brooding. 'I haven't thought about it.'

'There's still time,' she said urgently, feeling she was fighting for something precious. 'Perhaps that's where you've gone wrong. You had the idea fixed in your head that you loved Petula.'

'I do love her.'

'But how can you?' Gail burst out. 'She's like a painting—no, a painting usually has life. She's like a statue, beautiful but as cold as marble. She'll never be able to love you back in any way, because she's not a real woman.'

He hit her then, sending her staggering back across the room with a slap on her cheek. She felt a sharp stab of pain, as she came up against the heavy, old-fashioned dressing-table, but it passed. Nevertheless, she stared at him with shocked eyes. 'That's the second time!' she gasped, wondering what it was about her that moved him so easily to near violence.

'I'm sorry!' he muttered tersely, his eyes snapping. 'But Petula isn't what you think she is.'

Nervously Gail pushed aside the hair which had tumbled about her hot face. She had been wrong to criticise Petula, she must have asked to be slapped down, yet she couldn't offer more than half an apology. 'I shouldn't have said what I did,' she muttered stubbornly, 'even if I meant it.'

Strangely Carl didn't appear to be listening. His glance was riveted on the dark bruise on her forehead, which her hair had previously concealed. 'What the hell have you been doing with yourself?' he rasped furiously. 'I didn't do that!'

He mustn't have seen Mary. Gail wondered where she was. Indifferently she replied, 'I was thrown on Saturday, at the gymkhana.'

'You—fell?'

'Yes.' she tried to laugh at his sheer astonishment, 'Crazy, wasn't it? A hurdle no higher than three feet.'

'Have you seen a doctor?' he asked.

'Yes,' she nodded. 'Ann insisted. I saw Doctor Harding, but it's only superficial, nothing to worry about. He gave me some tablets in case my head aches.'

'Haven't you had it X-rayed?'

'Carl!' She tried to keep her hands off her throbbing cheek. 'What is this? I'm quite recovered.'

He frowned blackly. 'Are you?'

Gail lowered her eyes, biting her lip. Carl sounded impatient. Old habits die hard and he had always been concerned for his staff. But, whatever happened, he must be prevented from feeling it was necessary to consult Doctor Harding himself, and perhaps inadvertently discovering she was pregnant. He mustn't know about the baby now! Glancing at him quickly, she assured him, 'Doctor Harding's keeping an eye on me.'

'I hope so,' he said curtly.

'You really don't have to worry,' she insisted feverishly.

'I'm not unduly worried,' he rasped, a dull red creeping under his skin. 'It can become a habit, looking after someone, I suppose. Especially a girl as careless as you.'

That wasn't true. She was never that careless, but she didn't bother to deny it. Proudly she lifted her chin. 'Perhaps a divorce would be the best thing, then you won't have to bother any more.'

Carl's eyes flashed with sudden temper again, but he merely said harshly, 'I agree.'

'I'll leave the house . . .'

'I'd be grateful if you would,' he said roughly, 'and as soon as possible. Petula wants it completely done over before we come back.'

Gail attempted to envisage Deanly as Petula would change it. She had made few changes herself, liking it as it was. In time she might have switched some of the furniture round, bought one or two new pieces, but she couldn't think of that now. She couldn't think of anything but that her marriage was breaking up and she was helpless to prevent it. She might have managed to keep Carl from leaving her by confessing she was pregnant, but if she did that, he might eventually come to hate both her and the baby. And, if he didn't know about it, at least he couldn't take it from her.

'I quite understand,' she said stiffly, feigning coolness in an effort to hide her hurt.

'I'll make you an allowance, of course,' he continued. 'I'll see you don't starve.'

Thinking of the baby, Gail shook her head. If she took anything from him, he might want to see her occasionally, and that could be dangerous. It was a risk she refused to take. Anyway, she preferred to be independent. 'I'd rather not. I can work.'

Carl didn't argue. He merely said enigmatically, 'My solicitor will deal with everything.'

Gail couldn't help remarking sharply, 'How nice to be able to afford someone to deal with such tedious tasks!'

'I pay well enough,' he snapped arrogantly, clearly not caring for her tone. 'I realise you're feeling bitter, Gail, but I did warn you our marriage might not last, before we entered into it. It wasn't something we didn't discuss.'

She couldn't deny it. She had agreed to a marriage of convenience for the sake of Carl and Deanly and had been fully aware it might not last. Only she hadn't thought she would ever come to love him as much as she did, or considered the possible repercussions.

'I'm sorry,' she whispered miserably. 'You're quite right, of course, and if you want a divorce I won't do anything to try and prevent you from getting one. You won't forget Mary, though?' her mind veered unsteadily. 'She's been very kind.'

'She can caretake until I—we get back. I'll send her instructions.'

Suddenly, as if the sight of her pale young face

angered him afresh, his eyes hardened and he gathered up his things. 'It's no use prolonging this, Gail,' he said grimly. 'It can only get more painful.' Striding to the door, he barely paused. 'If we never see each other again, I hope you'll soon forget. And—good luck.'

'Goodbye,' she sighed bleakly, as his voice cut off with raw abruptness and she listened to his footsteps fading down the stairs. But it wasn't until the front door banged and his car started up that she realised dazedly the dreadful finality of it all. He had gone for good!

CHAPTER TEN

GAIL was never sure how long she lay on the bed weeping, but eventually she dragged herself off it and had a shower. Her body was aching so badly she would rather have had a soothing bath, but the shower did remove some of the ravages of tears from her face. Mary mustn't see how upset she was, although, she supposed, when she told her she was leaving, she might guess.

There was the future to be faced too, she realised, and a future without Carl seemed so empty she didn't want to think about it. Suddenly she was fiercely glad about the baby. No matter how hard a struggle it might be, bringing up a child single-handed, she would have something of Carl left. No one would take the baby from her, of that she was determined!

Yet despite such optimism, terror and pain washed over her in a frightening tide. However would she manage? How was she even to begin? In a few short months she had come to rely on Carl completely. True, there had been skirmishes, but in everything important she had let Carl dominate. Perhaps in doing so, she had exposed one of the weaknesses of her own sex, but now she felt that everything she had grown familiar with and loved was being swept from under her feet. She had taken advantage of Carl's strength and now she was going to have to pay for it.

Clenching tight hands, she strove for control as slowly she began to understand what it was like to feel totally bereft. She mustn't give in, that was the important thing to remember at the moment. Mary had to be found, the situation explained to her, if only briefly, and to do that without breaking down was going to take a lot of willpower.

Mary was in the kitchen, washing cabbage at the sink. Hearing Gail behind her, she spoke over her shoulder. 'I've been to Lambourn. One of the trucks was going and we needed a few things, but you would have found my note.'

'No,' Gail saw the note still lying on the table, 'I didn't look in the kitchen, but I wondered where you were.'

'Oh, dear,' Mary shook the surplus water off her hands then dried them. 'I was sure you would find it.'

Gail said unsteadily, as if by way of explanation, 'Carl was here.'

Something in her voice made Mary swing to really look at her for the first time. Gail had used make-up, but it wasn't enough to hide the marks of copious weeping. 'Good heavens!' she gasped, her eyes darkening with concern. 'What on earth's been going on? You say Mr Carl was here . . . Where is he now?'

'He went away again.' Gail's face went pasty white. 'He won't be coming back.'

'Good heavens!' Mary reiterated blankly, this time her voice a mere whisper. 'You can't mean . . .?'

As Mary gazed at her in appalled silence, obviously reluctant to put her fears into words, Gail took a deep breath. She had to tell her quickly. It was better to get the unpalatable things in life over and done with as soon as possible. Long ago she had discovered that.

It was difficult to even begin explaining without breaking down, but a merciful numbness spread through her body, enabling her to speak with some semblance of composure. 'Carl and I are going to be divorced, Mary. Petula Hogan—I should say, Oscar— has got a divorce and he wants to marry her. He intends bringing her to Deanly eventually. I'll be leaving, of course, but he would like you to caretake until he returns. His solicitor will be in touch. I believe his phone number's in the study.'

Mary groped towards a chair, sinking into it as she tried to digest Gail's jerky sentences. Clearly she had received a great shock. 'Oh, the fool!' she exclaimed angrily, for once too disturbed to use her usual discretion. 'If only I'd seen him!'

'It wouldn't have done any good,' Gail replied stiffly, still finding it difficult to tolerate a word against him, even from Mary.

'I might have been able to make him see sense,' Mary muttered.

Again, Gail shook her head. 'He loves Petula. It's been Petula all along, and now that's she's free, I can't stand in their way.'

'You ought never to have let him go!' Mary looked as though she could have said more on that point but restrained herself. 'She'll make his life a misery, though——' with a sniff, 'it might well serve him right for leaving you, especially the way you are! Didn't you tell him about your accident—and everything?'

'I told him about my accident,' Gail replied.

'But nothing else?'

'No!' Gail stared at Mary defiantly. 'What else could I tell him?'

Mary hesitated, then clearly decided to tackle what Gail refused to discuss another way. 'I won't stay here, after they come back, not if I were offered a thousand pounds a week! I'd never work for that woman, supposing she'd have me! I hate her, but the feeling's mutual. I saw too much of her when she was chasing Mr Carl! Will you be going to stay with your sister?'

Gail frowned. She hadn't got round to planning exactly what she would do. She had considered her future, but only in broad outlines. Ruth and Donald would take her in, but she couldn't live with them permanently. She had thought the same when her father died and they had offered her a home then. If they suggested it now she would refuse again, if for different reasons. Seeing them so happy together would be too painful a reminder of her own lost happiness.

'I might go to Ruth and Donald,' she said slowly,

'but only if it's convenient and until I can find a place of my own.'

'Wouldn't it be better,' Mary asked tentatively, 'if you stayed with them until after—well, you know? Girls nowadays are so independent, but even if you did find a place of your own, you'd need someone to help you nearer the time, wouldn't you?'

Suddenly Gail felt tears beginning to stream down her cheeks again, dissolving her hard-won composure. 'Oh, Mary!' she cried, sinking into a chair and burying her face in her hands on the kitchen table. She sobbed until she was completely exhausted, while Mary stood by, watching grimly, occasionally patting her heaving shoulders.

Gail knew Mary had guessed about the baby, and suddenly she didn't mind, as long as she didn't tell Carl. It made her feel terribly bitter that while both Ann and Mary had known what was wrong with her, such a possibility had never occurred to Carl. She might be relieved now that he didn't know, but she would never cease to be surprised.

After a few minutes, Mary made her some tea which she laced with brandy from Carl's study. 'Drink it up, there's a good girl,' she advised worriedly as Gail lifted her head to stare at it blankly. 'You can't neglect yourself now, you know.'

'Oh, Mary,' Gail clutched at the cup with trembling fingers, 'I wish I were dead! I feel I have nothing left to live for.'

Concern creased Mary's anxious face as Gail's distraught voice rose, but she betrayed none of it as she replied with calming firmness, 'That's not strictly true, dear—you have your baby.'

'Yes,' Gail agreed dully, making an effort to apologise, 'I'm sorry, Mary, for not telling you properly about being pregnant, but I only discovered myself on Saturday and I wanted to tell Carl first. Now he must never know. You must promise never to say anything.'

Mary nodded. 'He doesn't deserve to know, but I still

think he should. He shouldn't be allowed to escape his responsibilities so easily and it might have brought him to his senses, but I'm willing to abide by what you say.'

Gail said feverishly, 'I don't want any fuss, Mary. I suppose it's cowardly, but I'd like to get away before people discover what's happened. I couldn't bear the speculation.'

'I'm sure you'd get a lot of sympathy.'

Gail shivered. 'That would be even worse!'

Mary looked bewildered as if she couldn't understand this, but she merely said thoughtfully, 'It might be a good idea if you went to your sister's straight away, then no one need be any the wiser, for a little while, anyway. If anyone asks, I can just say you're visiting.'

Reluctantly, Gail nodded. She hated deception of any kind, but there seemed nothing else for it. 'I'll go tomorrow, if she'll have me.'

'It would be better,' Mary advised wisely, 'to stay with her until you get things properly sorted out. You never know, once you've had time to get over the shock of what's happened, you might decide to stay with her for good. It never pays to make decisions like this in a hurry. It's best to take your time.'

When Gail rang Ruth, Ruth said decisively that she must come immediately. 'Shall I ask Donald to fetch you?' Ruth didn't drive herself.

Gail was grateful, but assured her it wouldn't be necessary as she still had her own car.

'It's beyond me, how he could have left you!' Ruth exclaimed.

As it had seemed only fair to give Ruth some explanation for her visit, Gail had thought it might be simpler in the long run to stick to the truth. As briefly as possible she had outlined the situation, but she hadn't felt able to say much over the phone.

'I'd rather not talk about it just now,' she replied painfully to Ruth's disgusted comment.

Hearing her sister's voice shaking, Ruth, with quick comprehension, asked no more questions. 'I'll be waiting when you arrive tomorrow,' she said gently. 'We can talk then, if you feel like it.'

Leaving Deanly was one of the hardest things Gail had ever had to do. Always, before, when she had left it, she had known she would be coming back, but this time she knew she wouldn't be—she was going for good. Mary had helped her to pack, while labouring long and loud on how Carl would live to regret what he had done. Eventually, though she realised she meant well, Gail had been forced to beg her to stop.

'I still love him, Mary,' she had tried desperately to explain without causing offence, 'and I'm sure he didn't mean to hurt me so much. And in a way, I'm as much to blame as he is. He made no secret of his regard for Petula when he married me.'

Not being able to take her horse with her and having to go without saying a proper goodbye to the staff were just two of the other things which made Gail almost break down again and weep. It grew so painful that she was relieved when it was time for her to leave.

The weather was far from pleasant as she set off, but she barely considered it. Her thoughts were full of Carl. Secretly she had said goodbye to him in the room they had shared. She had stood in the doorway and looked at the bed, in which she had so often been held in his arms and known such happiness. There he had held her and kissed her, taught her what it was like to be a woman. Such experiences she knew she would always remember, with a gratitude which would eventually surpass all the bitterness she was now feeling. Nevertheless, as she had finally closed the bedroom door, her resentment against what fate appeared to be doing to her had risen almost violently.

It might have been because of this resentment, which lingered long after Mary had said an anxious goodbye and warned her to be careful, that she was careless. She must have been careless, otherwise she was sure she would have seen the motorist who shot out of a byroad straight across her path. Afterwards, although the police convinced her she'd had no chance whatsoever of employing avoidance tactics, she always carried with her some element of doubt.

Her doubts, though, were no harder to bear than the knowledge, when she recovered consciousness in hospital the next day, that she had lost her baby. Although she had been wearing the regulation seat-belt, it hadn't been enough to save her completely. It might have saved her from serious injury, but the terrible jerking she had sustained had brought on a miscarriage, and though help had arrived very quickly, it had been too late.

Ruth was allowed to see her, but only for a few minutes.

'Why didn't you tell me?' she cried, her face nearly as white as Gail's as she sat down beside her.

'I was going to when I arrived,' Gail whispered painfully. 'Oh, Ruth!' she choked, in sudden anguish, gazing at her sister desperately. 'I feel I've killed my baby!'

'No. Oh, shush!' having had strict instructions that Mrs Elliot mustn't be upset, Ruth hushed her frantically. 'You mustn't even think such things, darling. It was the other driver's fault, he was drunk, and there are plenty of witnesses who saw him dart over the road, straight at you. In fact a police car happened to be one of them.'

Gail refused to be pacified. 'I should have told Carl,' she wept. 'Mary said I should. If I had,' she breathed brokenly, 'he would have made me stay at home. Now he'll hate me because I tried to keep the baby for myself and I've killed his son!'

'Oh, darling!' Ruth found she was weeping herself and had to call the nurse. Gail was so distraught she was afraid for her. 'It wasn't your fault,' she repeated quickly. 'If anyone's to blame it's Carl. What wouldn't I give,' she exclaimed, her face hardening angrily, 'to be able to tell him exactly what I think of him!'

'No!' Gail's voice was hoarse with panic. 'I love him. You mustn't!'

'I don't suppose I'll ever get the chance.' Ruth patted her hand gently as the nurse came in, but with a glint in her eyes which might have betrayed to Gail, if she hadn't been too ill to notice, that she fully intended making sure she did, at the first opportunity!

'I don't want Carl to know, but do you think he should?' Gail asked feverishly.

'No,' Ruth replied firmly, moving aside to let the nurse take Gail's rapid pulse. 'You owe him nothing, and Donald and I will look after you.'

Ruth came to see her every day, bringing Donald with her. Apart from them, she had no other visitors as she was in hospital not far from where they lived, where she knew no one. Sometimes she felt ashamed that she didn't seem to care whether Ruth and Donald came or not. From near unbearable anguish, she had sunk into a dull but mercifully unfeeling stupor, in which nothing seemed to matter any more. She didn't want to eat or drink, and grew so painfully thin that at last her doctor spoke to her.

'A miscarriage is often followed by severe depression,' he said gently, 'and it's essential that you should try and fight it. You won't recover at once, but you will do in time.'

'I thought one couldn't fight depression,' she said woodenly.

The doctor, who had learnt something of Gail's circumstances from Ruth, looked at her compassionately. 'You can't just think yourself out of it, I agree, but to a certain extent we're mostly all capable of helping ourselves. In your case, you could make a start by trying to eat a little more and taking more interest in what's going on round you, then you might soon begin feeling better.'

After another week Gail was discharged from hospital and went home with Ruth and Donald. Physically she had made a good recovery, but although she had made a praiseworthy effort to follow her doctor's advice, she still felt half dead inside.

While she was in hospital, she hadn't had a visit from anyone at Deanly, but she had received a short letter from Mary. It was a rather odd letter, which puzzled Gail slightly, if she couldn't say exactly why. In it Mary had said how upset she had been when Ruth had rung and told her about Gail losing her baby. She hoped Gail was keeping better and as soon as she could think of a suitable excuse she would come and see her.

Gail had been too apathetic, at first, to wonder why Mary should feel she needed an excuse to get away. It wasn't until she left the hospital and remembered she hadn't replied that she began feeling curious about it. It couldn't be that Mary was frightened to leave the house empty, for Carl had frequently been away for weeks at a time, when he'd had no indoor staff, and no harm had come to it. Eventually Gail gave up wondering what Mary had meant and wrote back.

She kept her letter almost as brief as Mary's had been for she found even thinking of Deanly still hurt. She had intended saying only that she was well and staying with Ruth and Donald, so she was confused to find herself adding at the end. 'I often think of Carl, Mary, and wish he was here. He will always mean more to me than anyone. I can't sleep at nights for thinking of him, and I'll never forgive myself for losing his child.'

Staring aghast at what she had written, she almost tore it up. Then suddenly she didn't care. It had been a relief to bare her soul, and Mary would never tell anyone, she was discreet. Drawing a shaking breath, Gail thrust the single sheet into an envelope and went out to post it before she could change her mind.

The Vicarage, several miles, Gail discovered, from the south coast, was as large as Donald's previous one, so there was plenty to do. As she grew stronger, Gail helped wherever she could, taking over the cooking and most of the household tasks, thus freeing Ruth to assist more in the parish. She was grateful for the chance to keep busy because it prevented her from thinking of Carl continually.

One thing that bewildered her as the weeks crawled by was that she heard nothing from Carl's solicitor about the divorce. She didn't like to mention it to Donald as he appeared to avoid the subject. He might be frequently asked advice about it, but she knew he believed marriage should be for ever. To begin with, it hadn't seemed to matter, but the agony of waiting began to prove too much to endure. One day, in desperation, she rang Carl's solicitor's offices in London.

Carl dealt with a big legal firm and she was informed, after quite a long wait, that the man who ususally looked after his affairs was out. The second time she rang, the same secretary was again very vague. She said that she understood Mr Elliot was thinking of transferring his business elsewhere, and they could tell her nothing.

'I can't understand it!' Gail complained to Ruth, despair forcing her at last to speak to her sister. 'How can I discover what's going on if I don't know where to look? You'd think someone, somewhere, could tell me something!'

Ruth glanced at her carefully. Donald and she had just arrived back from London and she looked unusually tired and strained. 'I'd forget about it, if I were you,' she advised. 'I expect you'll hear soon enough, but if you don't, in another few months you could try again. You might be stronger by then,' she added quietly.

'I'm strong enough now!' Gail protested agitatedly.

'I don't agree,' Ruth replied flatly, gratefully drinking the hot tea Gail had made but which Donald had refused in favour of a shower. 'Do you think we haven't noticed you're still far too thin, how you look every morning as though you've cried yourself to sleep—if you sleep at all? I'm devoted to Donald,' she went on with frown, 'but I haven't your capacity for suffering.

Looking at you sometimes, I'm almost thankful that I don't feel things as deeply.'

Gail said, swallowing a sob in her throat, 'I can't help the way I am.'

'You can't still love Carl?' asked Ruth incredulously.

'How can I not?' Gail whispered helplessly. 'I think he'll always be part of me.'

'That's what I can't understand!' Ruth exclaimed, so suddenly furious that Gail stared at her. 'You were certainly crazy about him, and while he went off and left you, I could have sworn he wasn't indifferent. Once or twice I caught the expression in his eyes when he looked at you.'

'Wh-what sort of expression?' breathed Gail, her heart beating more rapidly than it had done in weeks.

'Lust,' Ruth retorted frankly, obviously thinking this no time to mince words. 'He wanted you, all right. I saw lust, need, call it what you like! But I would have been willing to bet my bottom dollar that there was love as well.'

Heat coloured Gail's cheeks, then faded to leave her paler than ever. 'You must have imagined it!'

'I must have,' Ruth agreed quickly, as if she was already regretting her outburst. 'I'm sorry.'

'I have to forget him.'

'I would advise you to—completely,' Ruth said forcibly, 'He isn't worth suffering over. Anyway, he's not going to get the chance to break your heart again!'

Ruth sounded so vehement Gail was startled, but she merely said bleakly, 'He wouldn't want one. He's with Petula now, and has probably forgotten my existence.'

'We must hope so,' Ruth snapped enigmatically. 'Meanwhile, I suggest you stop worrying and leave the divorce proceedings to him. No doubt you'll hear soon enough!'

The following evening, when Ruth and Donald had left for a parish meeting, to be followed afterwards by supper with friends, Gail sat down and made herself think about the future. Although she derived great comfort from the knowledge that Ruth and Donald loved her and appreciated her help about the house, she doubted the wisdom of staying with them forever. Yet what could she do? It would be laughable, if it wasn't so paradoxically unfunny, how the thought of returning to work with horses, which was the only thing she knew, filled her with the same fears which she used to believe prevented Carl from going to race meetings. Just as he had been reluctant to risk meeting Petula, Gail was apprehensive of meeting him. And she wouldn't need to go near a racecourse for that to happen. People who bred and worked with horses had the unpredictable habit of turning up anywhere!

A tear ran down her cheek, followed by others, but she made no attempt to stem the flow until she heard the doorbell.

'Oh, help!' she exclaimed aloud, thinking of some of Donald's well-meaning parishioners who might take one look at her and immediately enquire what was wrong. Frantically she scrubbed at her face with a pile of paper handkerchifs, hoping whoever it was might go away. Unfortunately the bell kept on ringing, and eventually, with a resigned shrug, she was forced to go and answer it.

Unconsciously inventing vague excuses for her untidy appearance, she opened the door. A cold, sore throat, or just not feeling so good? 'Hello,' she began, then stopped, suddenly, her eyes dilating, but before she could close the door on the man's face again, everything went black and she slid in a dead faint at his feet.

When she came round, she was lying on the sofa in the lounge with Carl bending over her—a Carl she scarcely recognised. Closing her eyes, a groan escaped her lips as she opened them again, but she wasn't having hallucinations. It was Carl, but he was so changed, she knew an immediate sense of shock.

As she stared up at him, the possible implications of his visit struck her in waves and her eyes widened in horror. Had he come to take her to task because their

divorce hadn't come through, or to annihilate her
because of the baby? He looked so dreadful, it must be
something terrible. When he didn't speak, her glance
wandered dazedly over his dark-shadowed eyes, the
colourless, sunken hollows of his cheeks, the thin-lipped
mouth, which never, even when Petula had deserted
him, could Gail remember looking so grim.

'I'm sorry,' she whispered hoarsely, forcing herself to
speak before he strangled her. She saw his hands curl
and expected to find them round her throat any minute.
'Is it about the baby you've come? I know I should have
told you the truth, but I didn't think you'd want to know.'

Her heart banged with fear when he didn't reply but
merely shook his head. Then she saw that he appeared
to be having some difficulty with his voice, because he
was swallowing convulsively. Transfixed, her stretched
glance rose slowly to his eyes again, and to her further
surprise they appeared to be damp with tears.

'Carl!' she gasped, for never during all the years she
had known him had he ever betrayed such emotion.
Temper and fury, amusement and arrogance, perhaps,
but never tears!

As if to confirm that she was seeing aright, he
brushed the back of a hand swiftly across his face.
'Gail!' he said brokenly, then paused, once more shaking
his head. 'It's no use,' he confessed with grim self-
mockery. 'Is there anything to drink in the house, Gail?
Without something to help me, I'm not going to be able
to start, let alone carry on. And,' he added thickly, 'you
look as if you could do with something yourself.'

She could, she nodded, indicating Donald's modest
drinks cabinet with an unsteady wave. 'Over there.'

She watched, taking deep breaths to try and stop
trembling as he poured two drinks and carried them
back to her. He waited until she had taken a sip of hers,
then drank his off in one go.

The whisky put a little colour in his cheeks, but he
was still shaking as he sat down beside her. 'I'm not
drunk,' he said hoarsely, 'unless it's drunk from the

pain and misery of wanting you and knowing I can never have you again.' His eyes, bitter orbs sunk in his face, darkened. 'You must hate me more than I ever imagined, when the mere sight of me makes you pass out.'

'Carl!' She was utterly confused by his obvious despair and anguish, which seemed as great as her own, 'I don't understand. Why should whatever we feel for each other concern you? You have Petula . . .'

He didn't let her finish. Jerking upright, he admitted, 'No, I don't.'

'You—don't?' Gail reiterated, her mind stupidly blank. What he said must be of the uttermost importance, yet she couldn't seem to take it in. 'You mean she left you again, as she did before?'

'No!' He made a violent movement, as if to take her in his arms, but withdrew sharply, as though fearing her revulsion, 'I left her,' he confessed.

Hysterical laughter rose in her throat, but she swallowed it down. So his conscience had troubled him, after all? But what comfort was she supposed to derive from that? What happiness would she find in having him back—if this was what he was offering, duty bound by her side, while clearly hungering after another woman.

'I suppose,' she said flatly, agony raking through her, 'you heard about my accident and felt guilty?'

'No!' his voice roughened sharply, 'I can't let you believe that. I didn't hear about you being involved in a car crash until I returned to Deanly, the day after.'

The day after? The pressure inside Gail was building up until she was suddenly unable to bear it. 'Why did you come back, then?' she breathed, her eyes anguished.

'I was halfway over the Atlantic,' he confessed harshly, 'when I realised what a fool I'd been.'

Gail felt so shocked somehow, she had difficulty in making her lips move. 'Where was Petula?'

'Sitting beside me.'

'Sitting beside you?' Gail's voice was more dazed

than ever. 'But why? What happened? What did she say?'

'Plenty, as a matter of fact.' Carl's voice was grim and he hesitated, as if he found it difficult to go on.

Gail licked dry lips. If he had discovered he didn't love Petula, that didn't necessarily mean he loved *her*. 'What made you change your mind?' she asked apprehensively.

His mouth twisted in self-contempt while his eyes looked tortured. 'We were on the plane, on our way to New York, when I realised I didn't love her any more. It hit me like a bomb that I'd never loved her, that nothing I'd ever felt for her even remotely resembled the feelings I had for you.'

Expelling a tautly held breath, Gail felt as stunned as Petula must have done, and a fleeting rage tore raggedly through her heart. 'Carl!' she gasped. 'You can't go round changing your mind like that! I suppose you and Petula were lovers.'

He went white to the lips. 'I've never been her lover, Gail, not even when I was engaged to her, all those months before I married you. It should have told me something, that I never wanted to go to bed with her, but I thought I was content to wait. You jolted me, that day, when you said she was as cold as a marble statue. I could have murdered you,' he confessed bleakly, 'but I saw on the plane that you'd only been speaking the truth. She's beautiful, but hard. If I'd married her my life would have been hell, though it would have been no more than I deserved.'

Her mind chaotic, Gail stared at him, trying to organise her reeling thoughts. 'If what you say is true,' she whispered huskily, 'why have you been so long in coming to see me? It's been almost three months!'

'That's not easy to explain either,' he replied grimly. 'I've never thought of myself as a coward, but I've been afraid to face you. After everything I've done to you, I believed you'd never want to see me again.'

'It wasn't all your fault,' she had said this before and

she would always believe it. 'You could have given me the chance.'

'It didn't seem that simple,' muttered Carl, the tortured lines on his face seeming to deepen even as she looked at him.

'You said you didn't know about the car crash until you got home again?' she prompted unsteadily.

'No,' he confirmed harshly, 'I didn't. Mary had apparently rung my solicitor to ask if he could find me. She told him you were seriously ill, but as I never left the airport in New York but came straight back to London, he didn't know where I was. I came straight home, for I was sure you would still be there. I imagined it would be a few days before you could get ready to leave, and I was going to beg you to forgive me and plead with you to stay. Mary, of course, believed I'd got her message, and when I asked where you were, she seemed to think I'd gone crazy. When I learnt what had happened—God!' he groaned, 'I'd never felt so bad in all my life!'

'Wh—what did you do then?' she whispered haltingly.

'Rang Ruth,' he answered tautly. 'She'd been speaking to Mary over the phone, but Mary had been too upset to think of asking exactly where you were. She could only remember Ruth mentioning a hospital on the south coast.'

'You rang Ruth?' Gail's eyes widened as they met his bleak ones. 'She never said . . .'

He shrugged, as if that didn't surprise him. 'Ruth told me,' his voice still reflected remembered pain, 'how ill you were and how you'd lost the baby. She said you didn't want to see me again and requested me, in no uncertain terms, to stay away from you.'

'Ruth—did?'

As Gail's eyes darkened with horror, he said thickly, 'You mustn't think too badly of her. I deserved everything she threw at me. I'd nearly killed you and I had no defence. She was only thinking of you.'

'You—you really believed I wanted nothing more to do with you?'

'It was very easy to believe you hated me,' he nodded tersely. 'I'd given you no reason to do anything else.'

Briefly, Gail closed her eyes, the pain of his absence still with her. 'You didn't think of coming to the hospital and finding out for yourself?'

'I came to the hospital,' he groaned, sweat breaking out on his brow which he wiped numbly away, 'I even spoke with your doctors. They didn't forbid me to see you—I imagine, anyway, I could have insisted, but I couldn't bring myself to face the hatred and contempt which I was sure was all you'd have left for me. But until you left it, I haunted the hospital. If anyone noticed they must have thought I was mad. I sat in the car-park for hours, just willing you to get better.'

'If only I'd known!' Gail groaned. 'I tried not to think of you because I believed you were with Petula. And apart from that, I felt terrible about your child. I'd wanted to keep him for myself, but instead I'd killed him.'

'Don't ever think that again!' Carl uttered hoarsely. 'I was more to blame than you, but it was you I was concerned for. After you left hospital and went to live with Ruth, I returned to Deanly, where I've been ever since.'

'Mary's been looking after you?' Gail's eyes dwelt on him hungrily; it was all she could do not to touch him.

'An unenviable task, I should think,' his lips twisted, 'considering how I've been.'

'Oh, Carl!' she whispered in anguish, 'I wish you'd come weeks ago.'

'You surely can't mean that?' he rasped, the bones of his face seeming to stand out harshly.

'I do,' she said softly, heartache forgotten. 'Whatever made you change your mind, I'll always be grateful. I——' her voice faltered, then strengthened as her eyes shone with a new light, 'I love you.'

His arms lifted uncertainly, then, firm and sure, they

went around her, pulling her to him. As though compelled by a force stronger than himself, he bent forward, his lips brushing hers with a wonderful gentleness.

'Oh, my darling,' he said thickly, holding himself, Gail could tell, under rigid control. 'Ever since I found the note I've been hoping, but it didn't seem possible that what you said in it could be true.'

'What note?' Gail gazed at him in bewilderment.

He sighed, his arms tightening, as if he found it difficult to believe she was in them. 'The one Mary dropped after she decided she needed a holiday and asked me to run her to the station. I found it on the hall floor when I got back, but it wasn't until I picked it up that I saw it was one which you'd written, apparently soon after you'd been discharged from hospital.'

'You—read it?' Gail's cheeks flushed nervously as she tried to remember what she had put in it.

'I wasn't going to at first,' Carl confessed, 'but the more I thought about it, the more convinced I was that Mary had dropped it deliberately, so then I did.' He drew a deep breath as Gail's eyes widened, 'I was glad I did, because afterwards I knew I couldn't stay away any longer. I had to see you, no matter what the outcome.'

'Oh, Carl,' she breathed, 'I'm glad you did, too. We have a lot to thank Mary for.'

'She must have thought I had suffered enough,' he reflected grimly. 'I don't know if I would agree,' he added heavily, 'but I've certainly suffered!'

'Carl,' she whispered gently, 'let's forget, for tonight anyway. There might be more things to discuss, but can't they keep?'

He needed no further encouragement, and as he strained her close, her body sprang to life. 'I love you and want you,' he muttered hoarsely. 'All the time it's been you. You plagued and tormented me, roused my love and passion. Now it all seems to be combining in a terrible thirst which is going to take a lifetime to quench.'

He gave an agonised groan as their lips met and their heartbeats increased from fast to a thundering gallop.

Then suddenly he was putting her from him and muttering thickly, 'Gail, let's go home.'

Gail stiffened, her uncertain gaze reflecting her anxiety. 'Home? You mean to Deanly?'

Carl nodded, his eyes darkening. 'I must have you there, my sweet. I want us to make a new beginning. Don't you want that too?'

'Oh, yes,' she flushed but nodded eagerly. 'It's only— well,' she hesitated, 'what about Ruth and Donald? They're out at the moment, but I shouldn't like to leave without saying goodbye. Ruth may not always act wisely,' she admitted, 'but whatever she does, her intentions are always the best. And she has been good to me.'

'I know,' tenderly Carl drew her to her feet then cradled her face between his two hands, 'I'll always be grateful, but I've some news for you. I rang her after lunch, when I found your note, and told her I had to speak to you. If you had answered the phone, I was going to plead a wrong number and keep on trying until I got hold of her.'

Gail stared at him in stunned surprise. 'What did she say?'

'Nothing much, actually,' Carl assured her. 'In fact, she said it might be a good idea, as you'd never stopped fretting.'

'She knew about Petula?'

'Yes. I told her in the beginning what a fool I'd been.'

Gail felt a stirring of anger that Ruth had hidden so much from her, but seeing her indignation, Carl shook his head. 'Let's begin again with Ruth, too, shall we?' he suggested gently. 'After I told her I had to speak to you, I also said that if by some incredible stroke of good fortune you were willing to forgive me, I was going to take you away.'

'And what had she to say to that?' Gail reiterated helplessly.

Carl grinned slightly, his eyes lighting with the first hint of humour Gail had seen in them since he came. 'She said to be sure and lock the door behind us as she didn't want to find the house ransacked when Donald and she got back.'

And so Gail and Carl returned to Deanly, through the wildness of an early October night, with the wind blowing falling leaves across their path, which they were too absorbed in one another to notice.

'I'm going to take you for a proper honeymoon,' Carl promised, 'somewhere where there'll just be the two of us.'

As the front door closed behind them, he drew her almost reverently into his arms. 'I'm still finding it difficult to believe you're really here,' he muttered, a terrible bleakness shadowing his strong features. 'These past three months have been hell. When I think of how I've made you suffer, especially over losing the baby . . .'

Swiftly she laid gentle fingers over his taut lips, cutting off any further self-recrimination. Never having expected to see Deanly again, she wanted nothing to spoil, what she considered, the glory of their homecoming. 'It's over now, darling.'

Tightly he retorted, 'I don't think I'll ever forget.'

'You will,' she promised. 'We both will, and we'll have other children.'

'Oh, Gail!' Carl pressed anguished kisses on her flushed cheeks and tremulous lips, 'I don't know why I didn't realise I loved you long before I did. All the signs were there. I began to hate it when other men looked at you; when Jeff did, I could have killed him! After I left you that last time, driving to London, I couldn't stop wondering if you'd go to him. I nearly went mad. I began to remember how every time I'd made love to you had been like a trip to heaven, and I thought I was going insane!'

'For me, it was you all along,' Gail said softly but very clearly. 'If you hadn't come back there would never have been anyone else.'

'I can still scarcely believe it,' Carl said bitterly. 'I don't deserve you, I must have spoiled everything.'

As his voice grew steadily grimmer, his eyes bleaker, she became aware that there was only one way she could restore his confidence and—yes, she was ready to admit it, the arrogance she loved. 'You could try showing me how much you love me?' she suggested, with a gently teasing smile. 'Then you might realise you haven't spoiled anything. Unless,' her eyes teased again, 'you'd rather have a cup of tea?'

'God!' A shudder ran through him, every bone in his body seeming to clench as he shook his head. 'I'm only thirsty for one thing!' With a sudden groan he swung her into his arms and carried her upstairs.

Crushed against him, as they reached the bedroom, Gail couldn't help being aware of how aroused he was. 'Oh, darling,' he muttered, holding her against the hardness of his thighs as she slid to the ground, 'I've got to have you. I was going to give you time, but I find I can't.'

'I love you,' she whispered, her arms curling tightly about his neck, her fingers entwined in his hair as scorching passion shot right through her. When his mouth took possession of hers, she responded wildly to the urgent pressure of his lips, her own opening eagerly to his.

Her clothes fell heedlessly to the floor as he peeled them off, his following. 'Tell me you love me again,' he demanded thickly. 'Tell me you love me and can't live without me, because life without you hasn't been worth living.'

The bed was soft to her bare skin as Carl's taut body crushed her down into its yielding depth. He was groaning her name, his hands, mouth and body mutely expressing his hunger for her. If she had ever had reason to doubt his love for her, now all doubt fled.

'I love you,' she heard herself gasping, until there was only the harshness of his breathing and her whimpers of delight.

'You're so beautiful . . .' His voice grew harsh and inarticulate, his murmurings interspersed with Gail's feverish declarations of love. She felt the weight of his desire, his body tense and vital, hard against her softness, and knew an ever-increasing surge of ecstasy. Then, like a tidal wave sweeping everything before it, longing claimed her utterly. She became alive beneath his hands, her slender limbs parting and lifting to meet his, and as he thrust himself on to her, he uttered an anguished cry and buried his face in the perfumed softness of her breasts. There was no time for lingering caresses, their desire was too urgent. Together they climbed to devastating heights until they were consumed simultaneously by a flood of fire which completely overwhelmed them.

Outside, the wind rose and seemed in tune with the wildness of their passion. Gail was like a flame in his arms, and, as he brought her to complete fulfilment, she cried out his name as the final spasm of rapture convulsed them.

Afterwards, when she managed to raise her heavy lashes and found him looking down on her, she was filled with gladness as she saw the old commanding light back in his eyes. But there was something else that thrilled her even more, a look of adoration and tenderness that hadn't been there when they had lain here before.

'I love you,' she murmured, for what she thought must be the hundredth time, but with such an expression of perfect trust that the man watching so intently swallowed involuntarily.

'And I you,' he murmured huskily, when at last he seemed able to speak. Then, drawing her to him, he began kissing her deeply again, showing her passionately how much.

Take 4
Exciting Books
Absolutely
FREE

Love, romance, intrigue... all are captured for you by Mills & Boon's top-selling authors. By becoming a regular reader of Mills & Boon's Romances you can enjoy 6 superb new titles every month plus a whole range of special benefits: your very own personal membership card, a free monthly newsletter packed with recipes, competitions, exclusive book offers and a monthly guide to the stars, plus extra bargain offers and big cash savings.

**AND an Introductory FREE GIFT for YOU.
Turn over the page for details.**

As a special introduction we will send you four exciting Mills & Boon Romances Free and without obligation when you complete and return this coupon.

At the same time we will reserve a subscription to Mills & Boon Reader Service for you. Every month, you will receive 6 of the very latest novels by leading Romantic Fiction authors, delivered direct to your door. You don't pay extra for delivery — postage and packing is always completely Free. There is no obligation or commitment — you can cancel your subscription at any time.

You have nothing to lose and a whole world of romance to gain.

Just fill in and post the coupon today to MILLS & BOON READER SERVICE, FREEPOST, P.O. BOX 236, CROYDON, SURREY CR9 9EL.

Please Note:- READERS IN SOUTH AFRICA write to Mills & Boon, Postbag X3010, Randburg 2125, S. Africa.

FREE BOOKS CERTIFICATE

To: Mills & Boon Reader Service, FREEPOST, P.O. Box 236, Croydon, Surrey CR9 9EL.

Please send me, free and without obligation, four Mills & Boon Romances, and reserve a Reader Service Subscription for me. If I decide to subscribe I shall, from the beginning of the month following my free parcel of books, receive six new books each month for £6.60, post and packing free. If I decide not to subscribe, I shall write to you within 10 days. The free books are mine to keep in any case. I understand that I may cancel my subscription at any time simply by writing to you. I am over 18 years of age.

Please write in BLOCK CAPITALS.

Signature _____

Name _____

Address _____

_____ Post code _____

SEND NO MONEY — TAKE NO RISKS.

Please don't forget to include your Postcode.

Remember, postcodes speed delivery. Offer applies in UK only and is not valid to present subscribers. Mills & Boon reserve the right to exercise discretion in granting membership. If price changes are necessary you will be notified.

6R   *Offer expires December 31st 1984*

EP86